THE HEART OF MAN

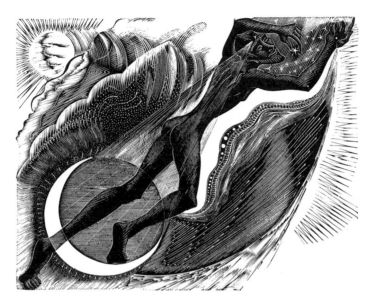

D.H. LAWRENCE
THE HEART OF MAN

An Illustrated Selection

Edited by Neil Philip

BLOOMSBURY

For Peter and Sylvia
NP

First published 1989 by
Bloomsbury Publishing Ltd, 2 Soho Square, London W1V 5DE

An Albion Book
Conceived, designed and produced by
The Albion Press Ltd, P.O. Box 52, Princes Risborough, Aylesbury, Bucks HP17 9PR

Editor: Robyn Marsack
Project Co-ordinator: Elizabeth Wilkes
Design: Emma Bradford, Paul Fielding

ISBN 0-7475-0456-3

The illustrations are reproduced courtesy of:
S. R. Badmin 91; Birmingham Museum and Art Gallery 93, 111; Bridgeman Art Library (Bradford City
Art Gallery and Museums) 61, (Christie's, London) 53, (Christopher Wood Gallery, London) 71, (Musee
d'Orsay, Paris) 66, (Howarth Art Gallery, Accrington) 25, (Private Collection) 86, 147; the Trustees of the
British Museum 3, 80, 132; Chris Beetles Ltd 37; Christopher Skelton 127, 131; Courtauld Institute
Galleries 143; Fine Art Photographic Library Ltd 34, 83, 114-115, 123, 135, 139, 163; Harry Ransom
Humanities Research Center, The University of Texas at Austin 130, 192; Hulton Picture Library 17, 32,
43; Penelope Hughes-Stanton 1, 84, 145, 177, 189, 191; Manchester City Art Galleries 19; the Trustees,
The National Gallery, London 98, 99, 106-107, 109; the National Portrait Gallery, London 10, 100;
Nottinghamshire County Library Service 14, 22, 45; Nottingham Public Library 51; University of
Nottingham 46, 47, 90, 150; the Octopus Group Picture Library/Constantino Reyes-Valero
(Photographer) 157; the Tate Gallery, London 48; Thyssen-Bornemisza Collection, Lugano, Switzerland
75; the board of Trustees of the Victoria & Albert Museum 171. All other pictures are from private
collections. The publishers would like to thank the staff of all the organisations listed above for their help.
The publishers acknowledge the kind permission of the copyright owners to reproduce works by S.R.
Badmin, Eric Gill, Blair Hughes-Stanton and Augustus John. Copyright in the work of D.H. Lawrence is
administered by Laurence Pollinger Limited for The Estate of Frieda Lawrence Ravagli, whose kind
assistance is here acknowledged. Every effort has been made to trace copyright owners, and the publishers
apologize for any inadvertent breach of copyright.

Black-and-white origination by IGS, Radstock
Typesetting and colour origination by York House, London
Printed and bound in Italy by New Interlitho

HALF-TITLE: *Fulfilment, by Blair Hughes-Stanton*
TITLE PAGE: *Glad Day, by William Blake*

Contents

Introduction

ALMOST THE first critical reaction Lawrence ever received was Ford Madox Hueffer's comment, on the manuscript of his first novel *The White Peacock*: 'It's got every fault that the English novel can have.' But Hueffer also recognised, 'you've got GENIUS.'

Hueffer's judgement holds true throughout Lawrence's turbulent and controversial career. Lawrence is one of the most original and vital of English novelists, but even his best work is seriously flawed. There is something somewhere in Lawrence to offend every taste and outrage every opinion. Yet with all his faults Lawrence *is* a great writer. He wrote three major novels: *Sons and Lovers, The Rainbow* and *Women in Love.* He was master of that fugitive form, the novella, in tales such as *The Fox, St Mawr* and *The Escaped Cock.* A volume of his best ten short stories could sit confidently next to that of any English writer bar Kipling. His many failed poems are outweighed by some of the most beautiful and compelling poetry of this century. His travel writings contain many delightful passages; all his works, even the manic, hectoring nonfiction, are instinct with fierce, passionate life.

He was born in Eastwood, Nottinghamshire, in 1885. His father was a collier; his mother had been a teacher. The years of his childhood and young manhood are reflected in *Sons and Lovers*, which he himself described as 'autobiography'. He trained as a teacher at Nottingham University College, and taught at Davidson Road School, Croydon between 1908 and 1911, when a recurrence of pneumonia forced him to retire.

The forces which moved Lawrence in these early years were complex. He despised his rough father, idolized his strong-willed, refined mother. He was devastated by the early death of his gifted older brother, William Ernest. Above all, he was tormented by the conflict between spiritual ideals and physical realities. The story of Paul and Miriam in *Sons and Lovers* is an image of Lawrence's relationship with Jessie Chambers, who wrote her own account of the same events in *A Personal Record.* In life, as in Lawrence's novel, the overpowering possessive love of Lawrence's mother overcame the usurper, prompting in Lawrence's mouth the bitterly remembered, corrosive words, 'I've looked into my heart and I cannot find that I love you as a husband should love his wife.' Later, Lawrence was to write to Jessie, 'They tore me from you, the love of my life. It was the slaughter of the foetus in the womb.'

The day before his mother's funeral, Lawrence and Jessie walked together 'on the familiar lanes':

> 'You know – I've always loved mother,' he said in a strangled voice.
>   'I know you have,' I replied.
>   'I don't mean that,' he returned quickly. 'I've *loved* her, like a lover. That's why I could never love you.'

His mother's death in 1911 was a shattering thing. This was 'the sick year':

> . . . in that year, for me, everything collapsed, save the mystery of death and the haunting of death in life. I was twenty-five, and from the death of my mother, the world began to dissolve around me, beautiful, iridescent, but passing away substanceless. Till I almost dissolved away myself, and was very ill: when I was twenty-six.

In the following year Lawrence made a complete break with this tortured past. He met and eloped with Frieda Weekley, the wife of one of his old teachers, recording the first phases of their explosive partnership in the verse diary *Look! We Have Come Through*. 'This is the best I have known, or ever shall know,' he wrote in 1913. His relationship with Frieda was stormy, but his fights with her were crucial to his development, a struggle towards equilibrium. During a severe illness in 1925, he told her: 'But if I die, nothing has mattered but you, nothing at all.'

In the early years with Frieda, Lawrence developed rapidly as a writer, discovering the power and flexibility of free verse and shaping *The Rainbow*, *Women and Love* and the first draft of *The Lost Girl*. He also made a number of key friendships, notably with the writers John Middleton Murry and Katherine Mansfield. But the waste and horror of the war years wrought a severe change in Lawrence's character and work. His mood and vision darkened, he became vehement and overbearing, and obsessed with power and leadership. He veered off course, on a self-conscious 'savage pilgrimage' in search of 'dark gods' which would redeem the futility of modern life. This restless unhappy mood is most evident in Lawrence's Mexican novel, *The Plumed Serpent*, though that novel also shows the vivid response to landscape which makes his writing on places as varied as Australia and southern Italy so compelling. The Lawrences never lived in England after 1919, though a brief visit in 1926 prompted a return to an English setting in *Lady Chatterley's Lover*, as if Lawrence recognized the truth of the admonition addressed to Gethin Day in the fragment *The Flying Fish*, by a sister who is significantly given Lawrence's mother's name, Lydia:

> 'Mind you don't wander into a cage one of these days . . . you would find far more room for yourself in Daybrook than in these foreign parts, if you knew how to come into your own.'

Though he wrote some fine short stories, and much interesting fiction and non-fiction, in these wandering years, his chief achievement was the verse of *Birds, Beasts and Flowers*, which celebrated his close observation of and affinity with the natural world, and which presaged the final death-bed flowering of his talent, in the *Last Poems* in which he did, without coming home, come into his own.

Dying of tuberculosis, wracked with a tearing cough, and so frail that he seemed to observers to be surviving on sheer will-power – 'like a flame burning on in miraculous disregard of the fact that there was no more fuel to justify its existence' – Lawrence found the rare courage to face with utter candour his approaching fate, when he should be 'dipped again in God, and new-created'. The sequence of poems which clusters round the long 'Ship of Death' is perhaps the best thing he ever wrote: lucid, brave, exquisitely controlled, and sharply poignant without a trace of self-pity:

> And if, in the changing phases of man's life
> I fall in sickness and in misery
> my wrists seem broken and my heart seems dead
> and strength is gone, and my life
> is only the leavings of a life:
>
> and still, among it all, snatches of lovely oblivion, and snatches of renewal
> odd, wintry flowers upon the withered stem, yet new, strange flowers
> such as my life has not brought forth before, new blossoms of me –
>
> then I must know that still
> I am in the hands of the unknown God,
> he is breaking me down to his own oblivion
> to send me forth on a new morning, a new man.

Lawrence died of tuberculosis at Vence on 2 March 1930, aged forty-four.

He chose as his personal emblem the phoenix, which renews itself in death, and this sense of renewal, so strong in the *Last Poems*, is present throughout his work. His concern is not being, but becoming: 'The history of the cosmos/ is the history of the struggle of becoming.' It is this theme which irradiates *The Rainbow*, taking it beyond realism. Lawrence wrote to his mentor Edward Garnett about the book in progress, 'don't look for the novel to follow the lines of certain characters: the characters fall into the form of some other rhythmic form, as when one draws a fiddle-bow across a fine tray delicately sanded, the sand takes lines unknown.' Earlier he had written:

> I have no longer the joy in creating vivid scenes, that I had in *Sons and Lovers*. I don't care much more about accumulating objects in the powerful light of emotion, and making a scene of them. I have to write differently.

In his essay 'The Future of the Novel', Lawrence wrote, '*What next?* That's what interests me. *What now!* is no fun any more.'

This urgent, passionate questioning, the attempt 'to get on with something really new', gives Lawrence's fiction much of its power. But the attempt to get away from the trivial details of life, to work out the consequences of Lawrence's exciting but dangerous 'belief in the blood', meant that the element of storytelling became less and less important. In the same essay on the novel, he continued,

> It seems to me it was the greatest pity in the world, when philosophy and fiction got split. They used to be one, right from the days of myth. Then they went and parted, like a nagging married couple . . . So the novel went sloppy, and philosophy went abstract-dry. The two should come together again, in the novel. And we get modern kind of gospels, and modern myths, and a new way of understanding.

As he pursued this course, his characters lose their individuality, and much of their human interest. Speech becomes rant. It is as if once Lawrence had found his voice, he was only able to shout in it.

That voice is nevertheless one of the most individual in English literature. It incorporated many elements, from his father's blunt, vivid dialect to the rhetoric and hymns of the Congregational Chapel. In the line of the English novel, Lawrence is the successor of Hardy, in whose work he most admired 'this setting behind the small action of his protagonists the terrific action of unfathomed nature'. This was a fruitful starting point for Lawrence's own fiction, which combines the Hardyesque novel with the new theories of the subconscious. But the restraint and discretion of Hardy's poetry offered no way forward for Lawrence, whose own verse in Hardy's mode is prissy and lifeless. It was the American Walt Whitman whose sinuous, exclamatory line showed Lawrence how to capture in verse 'the insurgent naked throb of the instant moment'.

At the very beginning of his career, while writing *The White Peacock*, and using his genius to cram it with 'every fault that the English novel can have', Lawrence told Jessie Chambers, 'I think a man puts everything he is into a book – a real book'. He wrote to Edward Garnett in 1913, 'I *know* I can write bigger stuff than any man in England.' In his middle period, when Lawrence seemed helpless in the spell of his own charisma, he wrote a good deal which was strident and unbalanced. But at its best, Lawrence's work in both prose and verse justifies both these statements. It resonates with pure wit, the wit of 'a man in his wholeness wholly attending'.

NEIL PHILIP
Princes Risborough, 1989

D.H. Lawrence, by Jan Juta

The Heart of Man

This short poem, published posthumously in the collection More Pansies, summarises Lawrence's central concern. He was interested in uncharted territory; the mysteries of the interior. Even the naturalistic settings and stories of his early work are there as context for the inner drama of the psyche. He was never a novelist of manners; nor was he really a novelist of ideas. He was, at his best and at his worst, a novelist of instincts; the first great writer to explore the subconscious.

The Heart of Man

There is the other universe, of the heart of man
that we know nothing of, that we dare not explore.

A strange grey distance separates
our pale mind still from the pulsing continent
of the heart of man.

Fore-runners have barely landed on the shore
and no man knows, no woman knows
the mystery of the interior
when darker still than Congo or Amazon
flow the heart's rivers of fulness, desire and distress.

Young Life

When French publishers required personal details for a preface in 1928, Lawrence wrote 'let them read Sons and Lovers, the first part is all autobiography'. For many readers this 'first part', with its vivid portrayal of the Lawrences' tense home life, is the best of Lawrence. It is a magnificent account of an England as individual and hitherto undocumented as Hardy's Wessex: what Lawrence later called 'the real England – the hard pith of England'. In November 1912, he described the finished work to his early mentor Edward Garnett:

It follows this idea: a woman of character and refinement goes into the lower class, and has no satisfaction in her own life. She has had a passion for her husband, so the children are born of passion, and have heaps of vitality. But as her sons grow up she selects them as lovers – first the eldest, then the second. These sons are *urged* into life by their reciprocal love of their mother – urged on and on. But when they come to manhood, they can't love, because their mother is the strongest power in their lives, and holds them. It's rather like Goethe and his mother and Frau von Stein and Christiana – As soon as the young men come into contact with women, there's a split. William gives his sex to a fribble, and his mother holds his soul. But the split kills him, because he doesn't know where he is. The next son gets a woman who fights for his soul – fights his mother. The son loves the mother – all the sons hate and are jealous of the father. The battle goes on between the mother and the girl, with the son as object. The mother gradually proves stronger, because of the tie of blood. The son decides to leave his soul in his mother's hands, and, like his eldest brother, go for passion. He gets passion. Then the split begins to tell again. But, almost unconsciously, the mother realises what is the matter, and begins to die. The son casts off his mistress, attends to his mother dying. He is left in the end naked of everything, with the drift towards death.

In later life Lawrence told Frieda, 'I would write a different Sons and Lovers now; my mother was wrong, and I thought she was absolutely right.'

PAUL WOULD be built like his mother, slightly and rather small. His fair hair went reddish, and then dark brown; his eyes were grey. He was a pale, quiet child, with eyes that seemed to listen, and with a full dropping underlip.

As a rule he seemed old for his years. He was so conscious of what other people felt, particularly his mother. When she fretted he understood, and could have no peace. His soul seemed always attentive to her.

As he grew older he became stronger. William was too far removed from him to accept him as a companion. So the smaller boy belonged at first almost entirely to Annie. She was a tom-boy and a 'flybie-skybie', as her mother called her. But she was intensely fond of her second brother. So Paul was towed round at the heels of Annie, sharing her game. She raced wildly at lerky with the other young wild-cats of the Bottoms. And always Paul flew beside her, living her share of the game, having as yet no part of his own. He was quiet and not noticeable. But his sister adored him. He always seemed to care for things if she wanted him to.

She had a big doll of which she was fearfully proud, though not so fond. So she laid the doll on the sofa, and covered it with an antimacassar, to sleep. Then she forgot it. Meantime, Paul must practise jumping off the sofa arm. So he jumped crash into the face of the hidden doll. Annie rushed up, uttered a loud wail, and sat down to weep a dirge. Paul remained quite still.

'You couldn't tell it was there, mother; you couldn't tell it was there,' he repeated over and over. So long as Annie wept for the doll he sat helpless with misery. Her grief wore itself out. She forgave her brother – he was so much upset. But a day or two afterwards she was shocked.

'Let's make a sacrifice of Arabella,' he said. 'Let's burn her.'

She was horrified, yet rather fascinated. She wanted to see what the boy would do. He made an altar of bricks, pulled some of the shavings out of Arabella's body, put the waxen fragments into the hollow face, poured on a little paraffin, and set the whole thing alight. He watched with wicked satisfaction the drops of wax melt off the broken forehead of Arabella, and drop like sweat into the flame. So long as the stupid big doll burned he rejoiced in silence. At the end he poked among the embers with a stick, fished out the arms and legs, all blackened, and smashed them under stones.

'That's the sacrifice of Missis Arabella,' he said. 'An' I'm glad there's nothing left of her.'

The Lawrence Family

Which disturbed Annie inwardly, although she could say nothing. He seemed to hate the doll so intensely, because he had broken it.

All the children, but particularly Paul, were peculiarly *against* their father, along with their mother. Morel continued to bully and to drink.

He had periods, months at a time, when he made the whole life of the family a misery. Paul never forgot coming home from the Band of Hope one Monday evening and finding his mother with her eye swollen and

D.H. Lawrence as a child

discoloured, his father standing on the hearthrug, feet astride, his head down, and William, just home from work, glaring at his father. There was a silence as the young children entered, but none of the elders looked round.

William was white to the lips, and his fists were clenched. He waited until the children were silent, watching with children's rage and hate; then he said:

'You coward, you daren't do it when I was in.'

But Morel's blood was up. He swung round on his son. William was bigger, but Morel was hard-muscled, and mad with fury.

'Dossn't I?' he shouted. 'Dossn't I? Ha'e much more o' thy chelp, my young jockey, an' I'll rattle my fist about thee. Ay, an' I sholl that, dost see.'

Morel crouched at the knees and showed his fist in an ugly almost beast-like fashion. William was white with rage.

'Will yer?' he said, quiet and intense. 'It'ud be the last time, though.'

Morel danced a little nearer, crouching, drawing back his fist to strike. William put his fists ready. A light came into his blue eyes, almost like a laugh. He watched his father. Another word, and the men would have begun to fight. Paul hoped they would. The three children sat pale on the sofa.

'Stop it, both of you,' cried Mrs Morel in a hard voice. 'We've had enough for one night. And *you*,' she said, turning on to her husband, 'look at your children!'

Morel glanced at the sofa.

'Look at the children, you nasty little bitch!' he sneered. 'Why, what have I done to the children, I should like to know? But they're like yourself; you've put 'em up to your own tricks and nasty ways – you've learned 'em in it, you 'ave.'

She refused to answer him. No one spoke. After a while he threw his boots under the table and went to bed.

'Why didn't you let me have a go at him?' said William, when his father was upstairs. 'I could easily have beaten him.'

'A nice thing – your own father,' she replied.

'"*Father*!"' repeated William. 'Call him my father!'

'Well, he is – and so –'

'But why don't you let me settle him? I could do, easily.'

'The idea!' she cried. 'It hasn't come to that yet.'

'No,' he said, 'it's come to worse. Look at yourself. Why didn't you let me give it him?'

'Because I couldn't bear it, so never think of it,' she cried quickly. And the children went to bed, miserably.

When William was growing up, the family moved from the Bottoms to a house on the brow of the hill, commanding a view of the valley, which spread out like a convex cockle-shell, or a clamp-shell, before it. In front of the house was a huge old ash tree. The west wind, sweeping from Derbyshire, caught the houses with full force, and the tree shrieked again. Morel liked it.

'It's music,' he said. 'It sends me to sleep.'

But Paul and Arthur and Annie hated it. To Paul it became almost a demoniacal noise. The winter of their first year in the new house their father was very bad. The children played in the street, on the brim of the wide, dark valley, until eight o'clock. Then they went to bed. Their mother sat sewing below. Having such a great space in front of the house gave the children a feeling of night, of vastness, and of terror. This terror came in from the shrieking of the tree and the anguish of the home discord. Often Paul would wake up, after he had been asleep a long time, aware of thuds downstairs. Instantly he was wide awake. Then he heard the booming shouts of his father, come home nearly drunk, then the sharp replies of his mother, then the bang, bang of his father's fist on the

D.H. Lawrence's birthplace, Victoria Street, Eastwood, Derbyshire

table, and the nasty snarling shout as the man's voice got higher. And then the whole was drowned in a piercing medley of shrieks and cries from the great, wind-swept ash-tree. The children lay silent in suspense, waiting for a lull in the wind to hear what their father was doing. He might hit their mother again. There was a feeling of horror, a kind of bristling in the darkness, and a sense of blood. They lay with their hearts in the grip of an intense anguish. The wind came through the tree fiercer and fiercer. All the cords of the great harp hummed, whistled and shrieked. And then came the horror of the sudden silence, silence everywhere, outside and downstairs. What was it? Was it a silence of blood? What had he done?

The children lay and breathed the darkness. And then, at last, they heard their father throw down his boots and tramp upstairs in his stockinged feet. Still they listened. Then at last, if the wind allowed, they heard the water of the tap drumming into the kettle, which their mother was filling for morning, and they could go to sleep in peace.

So they were happy in the morning – happy, very happy playing, dancing at night round the lonely lamp-post in the midst of the darkness. But they had one tight place of anxiety in their hearts, one darkness in their eyes, which showed all their lives.

Paul hated his father. As a boy he had a fervent private religion.

'Make him stop drinking,' he prayed every night. 'Lord, let my father die,' he prayed very often, 'Let him be killed at pit,' he prayed when, after tea, the father did not come home from work.

That was another time when the family suffered intensely. The children came from school and had their teas. On the hob the big black saucepan was simmering, the stew-jar was in the oven, ready for Morel's dinner. He was expected at five o'clock. But for months he would stop and drink every night on his way from work.

In the winter nights, when it was cold, and grew dark early, Mrs Morel would put a brass candlestick on the table, light a tallow candle to save the gas. The children finished their bread and butter, or dripping, and were ready to go out to play. But if Morel had not come they faltered. The sense of his sitting in all his pit-dirt, drinking, after a long day's work, not coming home and eating and washing, but sitting, getting drunk, on an empty stomach, made Mrs Morel unable to bear herself. From her the feeling was transmitted to the other children. She never suffered alone any more: the children suffered with her.

Paul went out to play with the rest. Down in the great trough of twilight, tiny clusters of lights burned where the pits were. A few last colliers straggled up the dim field-path. The lamplighter came along. No more colliers came. Darkness shut down over the valley; work was gone. It was night.

Then Paul ran anxiously into the kitchen. The one candle still burned on the table, the big fire glowed red. Mrs Morel sat alone. On the hob the saucepan steamed; the dinner-plate lay waiting on the table. All the room was full of the sense of waiting, waiting for the man who was sitting in his pit-dirt, dinnerless, some mile away from home, across the darkness, drinking himself drunk. Paul stood in the doorway.

'Has my dad come?' he asked.

Evening, by Isabel Codrington

'You can see he hasn't,' said Mrs Morel, cross with the futility of the question.

Then the boy dawdled about near his mother. They shared the same anxiety. Presently Mrs Morel went out and strained the potatoes.

'They're ruined and black,' she said; 'but what do I care?'

Not many words were spoken. Paul almost hated his mother for suffering because his father did not come home from work.

'What do you bother yourself for?' he said. 'If he wants to stop and get drunk, why don't you let him?'

'Let him!' flashed Mrs Morel. 'You may well say "let him."'

She knew that the man who stops on the way home from work is on a quick way to ruining himself and his home. The children were yet young, and depended on the breadwinner. William gave her the sense of relief, providing her at last with someone to turn to if Morel failed. But the tense atmosphere of the room on these waiting evenings was the same.

The minutes ticked away. At six o'clock still the cloth lay on the table, still the dinner stood waiting, still the same sense of anxiety and expectation in the room. The boy could not stand it any longer. He could not go out and play. So he ran in to Mrs Inger, next door but one, for her to talk to him. She had no children. Her husband was good to her, but was in a shop, and came home late. So, when she saw the lad at the door, she called:

'Come in, Paul.'

The two sat talking for some time, when suddenly the boy rose, saying:

'Well, I'll be going and seeing if my mother wants an errand doing.'

He pretended to be perfectly cheerful, and did not tell his friend what ailed him. Then he ran indoors.

Morel at these times came in churlish and hateful.

'This is a nice time to come home,' said Mrs Morel.

'Wha's it matter to yo' what time I come whoam?' he shouted.

And everybody in the house was still, because he was dangerous. He ate his food in the most brutal manner possible, and, when he had done, pushed all the pots in a heap away from him, to lay his arms on the table. Then he went to sleep.

Paul hated his father so. The collier's small, mean head, with its black hair slightly soiled with grey, lay on the bare arms, and the face, dirty and inflamed, with a fleshy nose and thin, paltry brows, was turned sideways, asleep with beer and weariness and nasty temper. If anyone entered suddenly, or a noise were made, the man looked up and shouted:

'I'll lay my fist about thy y'ead, I'm tellin' thee, if tha doesna stop that clatter! Dost hear?'

And the two last words, shouted in a bullying fashion, usually at Annie, made the family writhe with hate of the man.

He was shut out from all family affairs. No one told him anything. The children, alone with their mother, told her all about the day's happenings, everything. Nothing had really taken place in them until it was told to their mother. But as soon as the father came in, everything stopped. He was like the scotch in the smooth, happy machinery of the home. And he was always aware of this fall of silence on his entry, the shutting off of life, the unwelcome. But now it was gone too far to alter.

He would dearly have liked the children to talk to him, but they could not. Sometimes Mrs Morel would say:

'You ought to tell your father.'

Paul won a prize in a competition in a child's paper. Everybody was highly jubilant.

'Now you'd better tell your father when he comes in,' said Mrs Morel. 'You know how he carries on and says he's never told anything.'

'All right,' said Paul. But he would almost rather have forfeited the prize than have to tell his father.

'I've won a prize in a competition, dad,' he said.

'Have you, my boy? What sort of competition?'

'Oh, nothing – about famous women.'

'And how much is the prize, then, as you've got?'

'It's a book.'

'Oh, indeed!'

'About birds.'

'Hm – hm!'

And that was all. Conversation was impossible between the father and any other member of the family. He was an outsider. He had denied the God in him.

The only times when he entered again into the life of his own people was when he worked, and was happy at work. Sometimes, in the evening, he cobbled the boots or mended the kettle or his pit-bottle. Then he always wanted several attendants, and the children enjoyed it. They united with him in the work, in the actual doing of something, when he was his real self again.

D.H. Lawrence's father

He was a good workman, dexterous, and one who, when he was in a good humour, always sang. He had whole periods, months, almost years, of friction and nasty temper. Then sometimes he was jolly again. It was nice to see him run with a piece of red-hot iron into the scullery, crying:

'Out of my road – out of my road!'

Then he hammered the soft, red-glowing stuff on his iron goose, and made the shape he wanted. Or he sat absorbed for a moment, soldering. Then the children watched with joy as the metal sank suddenly molten, and was shoved about against the nose of the soldering-iron, while the room was full of a scent of burnt resin and hot tin, and Morel was silent and intent for a minute. He always sang when he mended boots because of the jolly sound of hammering. And he was rather happy when he sat putting great patches on his moleskin pit trousers, which he would often do, considering them too dirty, and the stuff too hard, for his wife to mend.

But the best time for the young children was when he made fuses. Morel fetched a sheaf of long sound wheat-straws from the attic. These he cleaned with his hand, until each one gleamed like a stalk of gold, after which he cut the straws into lengths of about six inches, leaving, if he could, a notch at the bottom of each piece. He always had a beautifully sharp knife that could cut a straw clean without hurting it. Then he set in the middle of the table a heap of gunpowder, a little pile of black grains upon the white-scrubbed board. He made and trimmed the straws while Paul and Annie filled and plugged them. Paul loved to see the black grains trickle down a crack in his palm into the mouth of the straw, peppering jollily downwards until the straw was full. Then he bunged up the mouth with a bit of soap – which he got on his thumb-nail from a pat in a saucer – and the straw was finished.

'Look, dad!' he said.

'That's right, my beauty,' replied Morel, who was peculiarly lavish of endearments to his second son. Paul popped the fuse into the powder-tin, ready for the morning, when Morel would take it to the pit, and use it to fire a shot that would blast the coal down.

Meantime, Arthur, still fond of his father, would lean on the arm of Morel's chair, and say:

'Tell us about down pit, daddy.'

This Morel loved to do.

'Well, there's one little 'oss – we call 'im Taffy,' he would begin. 'An' he's a fawce un!'

Morel had a warm way of telling a story. He made one feel Taffy's cunning.

'He's a brown un,' he would answer, 'an' not very high. Well, he comes i' th' stall wi' a rattle, an' then yo' 'ear 'im sneeze.

'"'Ello, Taff," you say, "what art sneezin' for? Bin ta'ein' some snuff?"

'An' 'e sneezes again. Then he slives up an' shoves 'is 'ead on yer, that cadin'.

'"What's want, Taff?" yo' say.'

'And what does he?' Arthur always asked.

'He wants a bit o' bacca, my duckey.'

This story of Taffy would go on interminably, and everybody loved it.

Or sometimes it was a new tale.

'An' what dost think, my darlin'? When I went to put my coat on at snap-time, what should go runnin' up my arm but a mouse.

'"Hey up, theer!" I shouts.

'An' I wor just in time ter get 'im by th' tail.'

'And did you kill it?'

'I did, for they're a nuisance. The place is fair snied wi' 'em.'

'An' what do they live on?'

'The corn as the 'osses drops – and they'll get in your pocket an' eat your snap, if you'll let 'em –– no matter where yo' hing your coat – the slivin', nibblin' little nuisances, for they are.'

These happy evenings could not take place unless Morel had some job to do. And then he always went to bed very early, often before the children. There was nothing remaining for him to stay up for, when he had finished tinkering, and had skimmed the headlines of the newspaper.

And the children felt secure when their father was in bed. They lay and talked softly awhile. Then they started as the lights went suddenly sprawling over the ceiling from the lamps that swung in the hands of the colliers tramping by outside, going to take the nine o'clock shift. They listened to the voices of the men, imagined them dipping down into the dark valley. Sometimes they went to the window and watched the three or four lamps growing tinier and tinier, swaying down the fields in the darkness. Then it was a joy to rush back to bed and cuddle closely in the warmth.

Paul was rather a delicate boy, subject to bronchitis. The others were all quite strong; so this was another reason for his mother's difference in feeling for him. One day he came home at dinner-time feeling ill. But it was not a family to make any fuss.

'What's the matter with *you*?' his mother asked sharply.

The Laundress, by Edouard Frere

'Nothing,' he replied.

But he ate no dinner.

'If you eat no dinner, you're not going to school,' she said.

'Why?' he asked.

'That's why.'

So after dinner he lay down on the sofa, on the warm chintz cushions the children loved. Then he fell into a kind of doze. That afternoon Mrs Morel was ironing. She listened to the small, restless noise the boy made in his throat as she worked. Again rose in her heart the old, almost weary feeling towards him. She had never expected him to live. And yet he had a great vitality in his young body. Perhaps it would have been a little relief to her if he had died. She always felt a mixture of anguish in her love for him.

He, in his semi-conscious sleep, was vaguely aware of the clatter of the iron on the ironing-stand, of the faint thud, thud on the ironing-board. Once roused, he opened his eyes to see his mother standing on the hearthrug with the hot iron near her cheek, listening, as it were, to the heat. Her still face, with the mouth closed tight from suffering and disillusion and self-denial, and her nose the smallest bit on one side, and her blue eyes so young, quick, and warm, made his heart contract with love. When she was quiet, so, she looked brave and rich with life, but as if she had been done out of her rights. It hurt the boy keenly, this feeling about her that she had never had her life's fulfilment: and his own incapability to make up to her hurt him with a sense of impotence, yet made him patiently dogged inside. It was his childish aim.

She spat on the iron, and a little ball of spit bounded, raced off the dark glossy surface. Then, kneeling, she rubbed the iron on the sack lining of the hearthrug vigorously. She was warm in the ruddy firelight. Paul loved the way she crouched and put her head on one side. Her movements were light and quick. It was always a pleasure to watch her. Nothing she ever did, no movement she ever made, could have been found fault with by her children. The room was warm and full of the scent of hot linen. Later on the clergyman came and talked softly with her.

Paul was laid up with an attack of bronchitis. He did not mind much. What happened happened, and it was no good kicking against the pricks. He loved the evenings, after eight o'clock, when the light was put out, and he could watch the fire-flames spring over the darkness of the walls and ceiling; could watch huge shadows waving and tossing, till the room seemed full of men who battled silently.

On retiring to bed, the father would come into the sickroom. He was always very gentle if anyone were ill. But he disturbed the atmosphere for the boy.

'Are ter asleep, my darlin'?' Morel asked softly.

'No; is my mother comin'?'

'She's just finishin' foldin' the clothes. Do you want anything?' Morel rarely 'thee'd' his son.

'I don't want nothing. But how long will she be?'

'Not long, my duckie.'

The father waited undecidedly on the hearthrug for a moment or two. He felt his son did not want him. Then he went to the top of the stairs and said to his wife:

'This childt's axin' for thee; how long art goin' to be?'

'Until I've finished, good gracious! Tell him to go to sleep.'

'She says you're to go to sleep,' the father repeated gently to Paul.

'Well, I want *her* to come,' insisted the boy.

'He says he can't go off till you come,' Morel called downstairs.

'Eh, dear! I shan't be long. And do stop shouting downstairs. There's the other children —'

Then Morel came again, and crouched before the bedroom fire. He loved a fire dearly.

'She says she won't be long,' he said.

He loitered about indefinitely. The boy began to get feverish with irritation. His father's presence seemed to aggravate all his sick impatience. At last Morel, after having stood looking at his son awhile, said softly:

'Good-night, my darling.'

'Good-night,' Paul replied, turning round in relief to be alone.

Paul loved to sleep with his mother. Sleep is still most perfect, in spite of hygienists, when it is shared with a beloved. The warmth, the security and peace of soul, the utter comfort from the touch of the other, knits the sleep, so that it takes the body and soul completely in its healing. Paul lay against her and slept, and got better; whilst she, always a bad sleeper, fell later on into a profound sleep that seemed to give her faith.

In convalescence he would sit up in bed, see the fluffy horses feeding at the troughs in the field, scattering their hay on the trodden yellow snow; watch the miners troop home – small, black figures trailing slowly in gangs across the white field. Then the night came up in dark blue vapour from the snow.

In convalescence everything was wonderful. The snowflakes, suddenly arriving on the window-pane, clung there a moment like swallows, then were gone, and a drop of water was crawling down the glass. The snowflakes whirled round the corner of the house, like pigeons dashing by. Away across the valley the little black train crawled doubtfully over the great whiteness.

Brinsley Pit

While they were so poor, the children were delighted if they could do anything to help economically. Annie and Paul and Arthur went out early in the morning, in summer, looking for mushrooms, hunting through the wet grass, from which the larks were rising, for the white-skinned, wonderful naked bodies crouched secretly in the green. And if they got half a pound they felt exceedingly happy: there was the joy of finding something, the joy of accepting something straight from the hand of Nature, and the joy of contributing to the family exchequer.

But the most important harvest, after gleaning for frumenty, was the blackberries. Mrs Morel must buy fruit for puddings on Saturdays; also she liked blackberries. So Paul and Arthur scoured the coppices and woods and old quarries, so long as a blackberry was to be found, every weekend going on their search. In that region of mining villages blackberries became a comparative rarity. But Paul hunted far and wide. He loved being out in the country, among the bushes. But he also could not bear to go home to his mother empty. That, he felt, would disappoint her, and he would have died rather.

'Good gracious!' she would exclaim as the lads came in, late, and tired to death, and hungry, 'wherever have you been?'

'Well,' replied Paul, 'there wasn't any, so we went over Misk Hills. And look here, our mother!'

She peeped into the basket.

'Now, those are fine ones!' she exclaimed.

'And there's over two pounds – isn't there over two pounds?'

She tried the basket.

'Yes,' she answered doubtfully.

Then Paul fished out a little spray. He always brought her one spray, the best he could find.

'Pretty!' she said, in a curious tone, of a woman accepting a love-token.

The boy walked all day, went miles and miles, rather than own himself beaten and come home to her empty-handed. She never realised this, whilst he was young. She was a woman who waited for her children to grow up. And William occupied her chiefly.

But when William went to Nottingham, and was not so much at home, the mother made a companion of Paul. The latter was unconsciously jealous of his brother, and William was jealous of him. At the same time, they were good friends.

Mrs Morel's intimacy with her second son was more subtle and fine, perhaps not so passionate as with her eldest. It was the rule that Paul should fetch the money on Friday afternoons. The colliers of the five pits were paid on Fridays, but not individually. All the earnings of each stall were put down to the chief butty, as contractor, and he divided the wages again, either in the public-house or in his own home. So that the children could fetch the money, school closed early on Friday afternoons. Each of the Morel children – William, then Annie, then Paul – had fetched the money on Friday afternoons, until they went themselves to work. Paul used to set off at half-past three, with a little calico bag in his pocket. Down all the paths, women, girls, children, and men were seen trooping to the offices.

These offices were quite handsome: a new red-brick building, almost like a mansion, standing in its own well-kept grounds at the end of Greenhill Lane. The waiting-room was the hall, a long, bare room paved with blue brick, and having a seat all round, against the wall. Here sat the colliers in their pit-dirt. They had come up early. The women and children usually loitered about on the red gravel paths. Paul always examined the grass border, and the big grass bank, because in it grew tiny pansies and tiny forget-me-nots. There was a sound of many voices. The women had on their Sunday hats. The girls chattered loudly. Little dogs ran here and there. The green shrubs were silent all around.

From inside came the cry 'Spinney Park – Spinney Park'. All the folk from Spinney Park trooped inside. When it was time for Bretty to be paid, Paul went in among the crowd. The pay-room was quite small. A counter went across, dividing it into half. Behind the counter stood two men – Mr Braithwaite and his clerk, Mr Winterbottom. Mr Braithwaite was large, somewhat of the stern patriarch in appearance, having a rather thin white beard. He was usually muffled in an enormous silk necker-chief, and right up to the hot summer a huge fire burned in the open grate. No window was open. Sometimes in winter the air scorched the throats of the people, coming in from the freshness. Mr Winterbottom was rather small and fat, and very bald. He made remarks that were not witty, whilst his chief launched forth patriarchal admonitions against the colliers.

The room was crowded with miners in their pit-dirt, men who had been home and changed, and women, and one or two children, and usually a dog. Paul was quite small, so it was often his fate to be jammed behind the legs of the men, near the fire which scorched him. He knew the order of the names – they went according to stall number.

'Holliday,' came the ringing voice of Mr Braithwaite. Then Mrs Holliday stepped silently forward, was paid, drew aside.

'Bower – John Bower.'

A boy stepped to the counter. Mr Braithwaite, large and irascible, glowered at him over his spectacles.

'John Bower!' he repeated.

'It's me,' said the boy.

'Why, you used to 'ave a different nose than that,' said glossy Mr Winterbottom, peering over the counter. The people tittered, thinking of John Bower senior.

'How is it your father's not come?' said Mr Braithwaite, in a large and magisterial voice.

'He's badly,' piped the boy.

'You should tell him to keep off the drink,' pronounced the great cashier.

'An' niver mind if he puts his foot through yer,' said a mocking voice

30

from behind.

All the men laughed. The large and important cashier looked down at his next sheet.

'Fred Pilkington!' he called, quite indifferent.

Mr Braithwaite was an important shareholder in the firm.

Paul knew his turn was next but one, and his heart began to beat. He was pushed against the chimney-piece. His calves were burning. But he did not hope to get through the wall of men.

'Walter Morel!' came the ringing voice.

'Here!' piped Paul, small and inadequate.

'Morel – Walter Morel!' the cashier repeated, his finger and thumb on the invoice, ready to pass on.

Paul was suffering convulsions of self-consciousness, and could not or would not shout. The backs of the men obliterated him. Then Mr Winterbottom came to the rescue.

'He's here. Where is he? Morel's lad?'

The fat, red, bald little man peered round with keen eyes. He pointed at the fireplace. The colliers looked round, moved aside, and disclosed the boy.

'Here he is!' said Mr Winterbottom.

Paul went to the counter.

'Seventeen pounds eleven and fivepence. Why don't you shout up when you're called?' said Mr Braithwaite. He banged on to the invoice a five-pound bag of silver, then, in a delicate and pretty movement, picked up a little ten-pound column of gold, and plumped it beside the silver. The gold slid in a bright stream over the paper. The cashier finished counting off the money; the boy dragged the whole down the counter to Mr Winterbottom, to whom the stoppages for rent and tools must be paid. Here he suffered again.

'Sixteen an' six,' said Mr Winterbottom.

The lad was too much upset to count. He pushed forward some loose silver and half a sovereign.

'How much do you think you've given me?' asked Mr Winterbottom.

The boy looked at him, but said nothing. He had not the faintest notion.

'Haven't you got a tongue in your head?'

Paul bit his lip, and pushed forward some more silver.

'Don't they teach you to count at the Board-school?' he asked.

'Nowt but algibbra an' French,' said a collier.

'An' cheek an' impidence,' said another.

Paul was keeping someone waiting. With trembling fingers he got his money into the bag and slid out. He suffered tortures of the damned on these occasions.

His relief, when he got outside, and was walking along the Mansfield Road, was infinite. On the park wall the mosses were green. There were some gold and some white fowls pecking under the apple-trees of an orchard. The colliers were walking home in a stream. The boy went near the wall, self-consciously. He knew many of the men, but could not recognize them in their dirt. And this was a new torture to him.

When he got down to the New Inn, at Bretty, his father was not yet come. Mrs Warmby, the landlady, knew him. His grandmother, Morel's mother, had been Mrs Warmby's friend.

'Your father's not yet come,' said the landlady, in the peculiar half-scornful, half-patronizing voice of a woman who talks chiefly to grown men. 'Sit you down.'

Colliers in a pub

Paul sat down on the edge of the bench in the bar. Some colliers were 'reckoning' – sharing out their money – in a corner; others came in. They all glanced at the boy without speaking. At last Morel came; brisk, and with something of an air, even in his blackness.

'Hello!' he said rather tenderly to his son. 'Have you bested me? Shall you have a drink of something?'

Paul and all the children were bred up fierce anti-alcoholists; and he would have suffered more in drinking a lemonade before all the men than in having a tooth drawn.

The landlady looked at him *de haut en bas*, rather pitying, and at the same time resenting his clear, fierce morality. Paul went home glowering. He entered the house silently. Friday was baking day, and there was usually a hot bun. His mother put it before him.

Suddenly he turned on her in a fury, his eyes flashing:

'I'm *not* going to the office any more,' he said.

'Why, what's the matter?' his mother asked in surprise. His sudden rages rather amused her.

'I'm *not* going any more,' he declared.

'Oh, very well, tell your father so.'

He chewed his bun as if he hated it.

'I'm not – I'm not going to fetch the money.'

'Then one of Carlin's children can go; they'd be glad enough of the sixpence,' said Mrs Morel.

This sixpence was Paul's only income. It mostly went in buying birthday presents; but it *was* an income, and he treasured it. But –

'They can have it, then!' he said. 'I don't want it.'

'Oh, very well,' said his mother. 'But you needn't bully me about it.'

'They're hateful, and common, and hateful, they are, and I'm not going any more. Mr Braithwaite drops his "h's", an' Mr Winterbottom says "You was".'

'And that is why you won't go any more?' smiled Mrs Morel.

The boy was silent for some time. His face was pale, his eyes dark and furious. His mother moved about at her work, taking no notice of him.

'They always stan' in front of me, so's I can't get out,' he said.

'Well, my lad, you've only to *ask* them,' she replied.

'An' then Alfred Winterbottom says, "What do they teach you at the Board-school?"'

'They never taught *him* much,' said Mrs Morel, 'that is a fact – neither manners nor wit – and his cunning he was born with.'

An Old Alley in Leeds, by Arthur Blackburn

So, in her own way, she soothed him. His ridiculous hyper-sensitiveness made her heart ache. And sometimes the fury in his eyes roused her, made her sleeping soul lift up its head a moment, surprised.

'What was the cheque?' she asked.

'Seventeen pounds eleven and fivepence, and sixteen and six stoppages,' replied the boy. 'It's a good week; and only five shillings stoppages for my father.'

So she was able to calculate how much her husband had earned, and could call him to account if he gave her short money. Morel always kept to himself the secret of the week's amount.

Friday was baking night and market night. It was the rule that Paul should stay at home and bake. He loved to stop in and draw or read; he was very fond of drawing. Annie always 'gallivanted' on Friday nights; Arthur was enjoying himself as usual. So the boy remained alone.

Mrs Morel loved her marketing. In the tiny market-place on the top of the hill, where four roads, from Nottingham and Derby, Ilkeston and Mansfield, meet, many stalls were erected. Brakes ran in from surrounding villages. The market-place was full of women, the streets packed with men. It was amazing to see so many men everywhere in the streets. Mrs Morel usually quarrelled with her lace woman, sympathized with her fruit man – who was a gabey, but his wife was a bad un – laughed with the fish man – who was a scamp but so droll – put the linoleum man in his place, was cold with the odd-wares man, and only went to the crockery man when she was driven – or drawn by the cornflowers on a little dish; then she was coldly polite.

'I wondered how much that little dish was,' she said.

'Sevenpence to you.'

'Thank you.'

She put the dish down and walked away; but she could not leave the market-place without it. Again she went by where the pots lay coldly on the floor, and she glanced at the dish furtively, pretending not to.

She was a little woman in a bonnet and black costume. Her bonnet was in its third year; it was a great grievance to Annie.

'Mother!' the girl implored, 'don't wear that nubbly little bonnet.'

'Then what else shall I wear,' replied the mother tartly. 'And I'm sure it's right enough.'

It had started with a tip; then had had flowers; now was reduced to black lace and a bit of jet.

'It looks rather come down,' said Paul. 'Couldn't you give it a pick-me-up?'

'I'll jowl your head for impudence,' said Mrs Morel, and she tied the strings of the black bonnet valiantly under her chin.

She glanced at the dish again. Both she and her enemy, the pot man, had an uncomfortable feeling, as if there were something between them. Suddenly he shouted:

'Do you want it for fivepence?'

She started. Her heart hardened; but then she stooped and took up her dish.

'I'll have it,' she said.

'Yer'll do me the favour, like?' he said. 'Yer'd better spit in it, like yer do when y'ave something give yer.'

Mrs Morel paid him the fivepence in a cold manner.

'I don't see you give it me,' she said. 'You wouldn't let me have it for fivepence if you didn't want to.'

'In this flamin', scrattlin' place you may count yerself lucky if you can give your things away,' he growled.

'Yes; there are bad times, and good,' said Mrs Morel.

But she had forgiven the pot man. They were friends. She dare now finger his pots. So she was happy.

Paul was waiting for her. He loved her home-coming. She was always her best so – triumphant, tired, laden with parcels, feeling rich in spirit. He heard her quick, light step in the entry and looked up from his drawing.

'Oh!' she sighed, smiling at him from the doorway.

'My word, you *are* loaded!' he exclaimed, putting down his brush.

'I am!' she gasped. 'That brazen Annie said she'd meet me. *Such* a weight!'

She dropped her string bag and her packages on the table.

'Is the bread done?' she asked, going to the oven.

'The last one is soaking,' he replied. 'You needn't look, I've not forgotten it.'

'Oh, that pot man!' she said, closing the oven door. 'You know what a wretch I've said he was? Well, I don't think he's quite so bad.'

'Don't you?'

The boy was attentive to her. She took off her little black bonnet.

'No, I think he can't make any money – well, it's everybody's cry alike nowadays – and it makes him disagreeable.'

'It would *me*,' said Paul.

'Well, one can't wonder at it. And he let me have – how much do you

Miss Lydiard's Stall, Bath, by Walter Tyndale

think he let me have *this* for?'

She took the dish out of its rag of newspaper, and stood looking on it with joy.

'Show me' said Paul.

The two stood together gloating over the dish.

'I *love* cornflowers on things,' said Paul.

'Yes, and I thought of the teapot you bought me –'

'One and three,' said Paul.

'Fivepence!'

'It's not enough, mother.'

'No. Do you know, I fairly sneaked off with it. But I'd been extraga-vant, I couldn't afford any more. And he needn't have let me have it if he hadn't wanted to.'

'No, he needn't, need he,' said Paul, and the two comforted each other from the fear of having robbed the pot man.

'We c'n have stewed fruit in it,' said Paul.

'Or custard, or a jelly,' said his mother.

'Or radishes and lettuce,' said he.

'Don't forget that bread,' she said, her voice bright with glee.

Paul looked in the oven; tapped the loaf on the base.

'It's done,' he said, giving it to her.

She tapped it also.

'Yes,' she replied, going to unpack her bag. 'Oh, and I'm a wicked, extravagant woman. I know I s'll come to want.'

He hopped to her side eagerly, to see her latest extravagance. She unfolded another lump of newspaper and disclosed some roots of pansies and of crimson daisies.

'Four penn'orth!' she moaned.

'How *cheap*,' he cried.

'Yes, but I couldn't afford it this week of all weeks.'

'But lovely!' he cried.

'Aren't they!' she exclaimed, giving way to pure joy. 'Paul, look at this yellow one, isn't it – and a face just like an old man!'

'Just!' cried Paul, stooping to sniff. 'And smells that nice! But he's a bit splashed.'

He ran in the scullery, came back with the flannel, and carefully washed the pansy.

'*Now* look at him now he's wet!' he said.

'Yes!' she exclaimed, brimful of satisfaction.

The Wild Common

'The Wild Common' is one of Lawrence's earliest poems, written about 1905. This is the first published text. Lawrence later revised this poem, as he did much of his early work, for the Collected Poems of 1928. He wrote then, '"The Wild Common" was very early and very confused. I have re-written some of it, and added some, till it seems complete. It has taken me twenty years to say what I started to say, incoherently, when I was nineteen, in this poem.' But the revised version is no more coherent and much less specific, and omits, too, the telling simile 'my soul like a passionate woman'.

The Wild Common

The quick sparks on the gorse bushes are leaping,
Little jets of sunlight-texture imitating flame;
Above them, exultant, the peewits are sweeping:
They are lords of the desolate wastes of sadness their
    screamings proclaim.

Rabbits, handfuls of brown earth, lie
Low-rounded on the mournful grass they have bitten down to the quick.
Are they asleep? – Are they alive? – Now see, when I
Move my arms the hill bursts and heaves under their spurting kick.

The common flaunts bravely; but below, from the rushes
Crowds of glittering king-cups surge to challenge the
    blossoming bushes;
There the lazy streamlet pushes
Its curious course mildly; here it wakes again, leaps, laughs, and gushes.

A Pond, by Myles Birket Foster

Into a deep pond, an old sheep-dip,
Dark, overgrown with willows, cool, with the brook
    ebbing through so slow;
Naked on the steep, soft lip
Of the bank I stand watching my own white shadow
    quivering to and fro.

What if the gorse flowers shrivelled and kissing were lost?
Without the pulsing waters, where were the marigolds and
    the songs of the brook?
If my veins and my breasts with love embossed
Withered, my insolent soul would be gone like flowers that
    the hot wind took.

So my soul like a passionate woman turns,
Filled with remorseful terror to the man she scorned,
    and her love
For myself in my own eyes' laughter burns,
Runs ecstatic over the pliant folds rippling down to my
    belly from the breast-lights above.

Over my sunlit skin the warm, clinging air,
Rich with the songs of seven larks singing at once,
    goes kissing me glad.
And the soul of the wind and my blood compare
Their wandering happiness, and the wind, wasted in liberty
    drifts on and is sad.

Oh but the water loves me and folds me,
Plays with me, sways me, lifts me and sinks me as though
    it were living blood,
Blood of a heaving woman who holds me,
Owning my supple body a rare glad thing, supremely good.

Lad-and-Girl Love

'Miriam' is the girl who, in Lawrence's synopsis, fights for the soul of Paul Morel. Her real name was Jessie Chambers, and she lived at Haggs Farm, just north of Eastwood. It was Jessie who encouraged Lawrence to write, and for some years she was his only reader. She was deeply hurt by his portrayal of their relationship in Sons and Lovers, *and never spoke or wrote to Lawrence again. Towards the end of his life Lawrence wrote to her brother, J.D. Chambers:*

> Whatever I forget, I shall never forget the Haggs – I loved it so. I loved to come to you all, it really was a new life began in me there …. Oh, I'd love to be nineteen again, and coming up through the Warren and catching the first glimpse of the buildings …. whatever else I am, I am somewhere still the same Bert who rushed with such joy to the Haggs.

After his death, Jessie wrote to Helen Corke:

> On the morning of the day he died, he suddenly said to me, as distinctly as if he had been here in the room with me: 'Can you remember only the pain and none of the joy?' And his voice was so full of reproach that I made haste to assure him that I *did* remember the joy. Then later on in a strange confused way he said – 'What has it all been about?'

Jessie's version of their story, A Personal Record, *is one of the most moving and illuminating of the many memoirs of Lawrence.*

PAUL HAD been many times up to Willey Farm during the autumn. He was friends with the two youngest boys. Edgar, the eldest, would not condescend at first. And Miriam also refused to be approached. She was afraid of being set at nought, as by her own brothers. The girl was romantic in her soul. Everywhere was a Walter Scott heroine being loved by men with helmets or with plumes in their caps. She herself was something of a princess turned into a swine-girl, in her own imagination.

42

Haggs Farm, the home of Jessie Chambers (Miriam)

And she was afraid lest this boy, who, nevertheless, looked something like a Walter Scott hero, who could paint and speak French, and knew what algebra meant, and who went by train to Nottingham every day, might consider her simply as the swine-girl, unable to perceive the princess beneath; so she held aloof.

Her great companion was her mother. They were both brown-eyed, and inclined to be mystical, such women as treasure religion inside them, breathe it in their nostrils, and see the whole of life in a mist thereof. So to Miriam, Christ and God made one great figure, which she loved tremblingly and passionately when a tremendous sunset burned out the western sky, and Ediths, and Lucys, and Rowenas, Brian de Bois Guilberts, Rob Roys and Guy Mannerings, rustled the sunny leaves in the morning, or sat in her bedroom aloft, alone, when it snowed. That was life to her. For the rest, she drudged in the house, which work she would not have minded had not her clean red floor been mucked up immediately by the trampling farm-boots of her brothers. She madly wanted her little brother of four to let her swathe him and stifle him in her love; she went to church reverently, with bowed head, and quivered in anguish from the vulgarity of the other choir-girls and from the common-sounding voice of the curate; she fought with her brothers, whom she considered brutal louts; and she held not her father in too high esteem because he did not carry any mystical ideas cherished in his heart, but only wanted to have as easy a time as he could, and his meals when he was ready for them.

She hated her position as a swine-girl. She wanted to be considered. She wanted to learn, thinking that if she could read, as Paul said he could read, 'Colomba', or the 'Voyage autour de ma Chambre', the world would have a different face for her and a deepened respect. She could not be princess by wealth or standing. So she was mad to have learning whereon to pride herself. For she was different from other folk, and must not be scooped up among the common fry. Learning was the only distinction to which she thought to aspire.

Her beauty – that of a shy, wild, quiveringly sensitive thing – seemed nothing to her. Even her soul, so strong for rhapsody, was not enough. She must have something to reinforce her pride, because she felt different from other people. Paul she eyed rather wistfully. On the whole, she scorned the male sex. But here was a new specimen, quick, light, graceful, who could be gentle and who could be sad, and who was clever, and who knew a lot, and who had a death in the family. The boy's poor morsel of learning exalted him almost sky-high in her esteem. Yet she tried hard to scorn him, because he would not see in her the princess but only the swine-girl. And he scarcely observed her.

Then he was so ill, and she felt he would be weak. Then she would be stronger than he. Then she could love him. If she could be mistress of

Felley Mill Pond

him in his weakness, take care of him, if he could depend on her, if she could, as it were, have him in her arms, how she would love him!

As soon as the skies brightened and the plum-blossom was out, Paul drove off in the milkman's heavy float up to Willey Farm. Mr Leivers shouted in a kindly fashion at the boy, then clicked to the horse as they climbed the hill slowly, in the freshness of the morning. White clouds went on their way, crowding to the back of the hills that were rousing in the spring-time. The water of Nethermere lay below, very blue against the seared meadows and the thorn-trees.

It was four and a half miles' drive. Tiny buds on the hedges, vivid as copper-green, were opening into rosettes; and thrushes called, and blackbirds shrieked and scolded. It was a new, glamorous world.

Miriam, peeping through the kitchen window, saw the horse walk through the big white gate into the farmyard that was backed by the oak-wood, still bare. Then a youth in a heavy overcoat climbed down. He put up his hands for the whip and the rug that the good-looking, ruddy farmer handed down to him.

Miriam appeared in the doorway. She was nearly sixteen, very beautiful, with her warm colouring, her gravity, her eyes dilating suddenly like an ecstasy.

Jessie Chambers, on whom Miriam is based

'I say,' said Paul, turning shyly aside, 'your daffodils are nearly out. Isn't it early? But don't they look cold?'

'Cold!' said Miriam, in her musical, caressing voice.

'The green on their buds – ' and he faltered into silence timidly.

'Let me take the rug,' said Miriam over-gently.

'I can carry it,' he answered, rather injured. But he yielded it to her.

Then Mrs Leivers appeared.

'I'm sure you're tired and cold,' she said. 'Let me take your coat. It *is* heavy. You mustn't walk far in it.

She helped him off with his coat. He was quite unused to such attention. She was almost smothered under its weight.

'Why, mother,' laughed the farmer as he passed through the kitchen, swinging the great milk-churns, 'you've got almost more than you can manage there.'

She beat up the sofa cushions for the youth.

D.H. Lawrence aged 21

The kitchen was very small and irregular. The farm had been originally a labourer's cottage. And the furniture was old and battered. But Paul loved it – loved the sack-bag that formed the hearthrug, and the funny little corner under the stairs, and the small window deep in the corner, through which, bending a little, he could see the plum-trees in the back-garden and the lovely round hills beyond.

'Won't you lie down?' said Mrs Leivers.

King Cophetua and the Beggar-Maid,
by Sir Edward Burne-Jones

'Oh no; I'm not tired,' he said. 'Isn't it lovely coming out, don't you think? I saw a sloe-bush in blossom and a lot of celandines. I'm glad it's sunny.'

'Can I give you something to eat or to drink?'

'No, thank you.'

'How's your mother?'

'I think she's tired now. I think she's had too much to do. Perhaps in a little while she'll go to Skegness with me. Then she'll be able to rest. I s'll be glad if she can.'

'Yes,' replied Mrs Leivers. 'It's a wonder she isn't ill herself.'

Miriam was moving about preparing dinner. Paul watched everything that happened. His face was pale and thin, but his eyes were quick and bright with life as ever. He watched the strange, almost rhapsodic way in which the girl moved about, carrying a great stew-jar to the oven, or looking in the saucepan. The atmosphere was different from that of his own home, where everything seemed so ordinary. When Mr Leivers called loudly outside to the horse, that was reaching over to feed on the rose-bushes in the garden, the girl started, looked round with dark eyes, as if something had come breaking in on her world. There was a sense of silence inside the house and out. Miriam seemed as in some dreamy tale, a maiden in bondage, her spirit dreaming in a land far away and magical. And her discoloured, old blue frock and her broken boots seemed only like the romantic rags of King Cophetua's beggar-maid.

She suddenly became aware of his keen blue eyes upon her, taking her all in. Instantly her broken boots and her frayed old frock hurt her. She resented his seeing everything. Even he knew that her stocking was not pulled up. She went into the scullery, blushing deeply. And afterwards her hands trembled slightly at her work. She nearly dropped all she handled. When her inside dream was shaken, her body quivered with trepidation. She resented that he saw so much.

The Bride

'The Bride' is one of several poems to Lawrence's mother written immediately
after her death, and shown to Jessie Chambers on the day before her funeral. At
her deathbed he had written, 'my mother is a sight to see and be silent about for
ever'.

The Bride

My love looks like a girl tonight,
   But she is old.
The plaits that lie along her pillow
   Are not gold,
But threaded with filigree silver,
   And uncanny cold.

She looks like a young maiden, since her brow
   Is smooth and fair,
Her cheeks are very smooth, her eyes are closed.
   She sleeps a rare
Still winsome sleep, so still, and so composed.

Nay, but she sleeps like a bride, and dreams her dreams
   Of perfect things.
She lies at last, the darling, in the shape of her dream,
   And her dead mouth sings
By its shape, like the thrushes in clear evenings.

D.H. Lawrence's mother shortly before her death

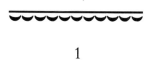

The White Stocking

'The White Stocking' was based on an anecdote told by Lawrence's mother. It is one of his earliest short stories, and was one of three entered for a competition in the Nottinghamshire Guardian at Christmas 1907 ('A Prelude' won, and was printed under Jessie Chambers's name). 'The White Stocking' was eventually published in revised form in The Smart Set in 1914, and included in Lawrence's first collection, The Prussian Officer. It describes the sort of situation and relationships one finds in Hardy's short stories, and the treatment is not unlike his. But there is, in the raw animal quality of Teddy and Elsie's relationship, a hint of the development to come. Lawrence understood both Elsie's taunting and Teddy's violence, and their consequences. He told Dorothy Brett, 'You have no idea, Brett, how humiliating it is to beat a woman; afterwards one feels simply humiliated.'

1

'I'M GETTING up, Teddilinks,' said Mrs Whiston, and she sprang out of bed briskly.

'What the Hanover's got you?' asked Whiston.

'Nothing. Can't I get up?' she replied animatedly.

It was about seven o'clock, scarcely light yet in the cold bedroom. Whiston lay still and looked at his wife. She was a pretty little thing, with her fleecy short black hair all tousled. He watched her as she dressed quickly, flicking her small delightful limbs, throwing her clothes about her. Her slovenliness and untidiness did not trouble him. When she picked up the edge of her petticoat, ripped off a torn string of white lace, and flung it on the dressing-table, her careless abandon made his spirit glow. She stood before the mirror and roughly scrambled together her profuse little mane of hair. He watched the quickness and softness of her

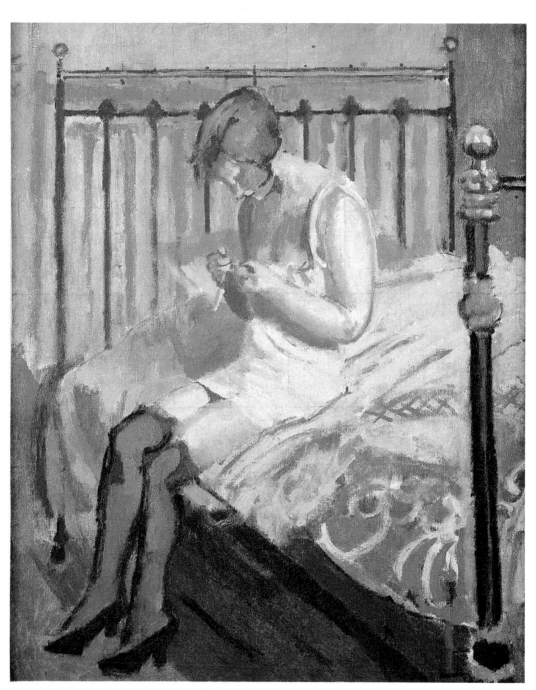

Yvonne, by Walter Sickert

She wore her earrings all morning, in the house. She was self-conscious, and quite brilliantly winsome, when the baker came, wondering if he would notice. All the tradesmen left her door with a glow in them, feeling elated, and unconsciously favouring the delightful little creature, though there had been nothing to notice in her behaviour.

She was stimulated all the day. She did not think about her husband. He was the permanent basis from which she took these giddy light flights into nowhere. At night, like chickens and curses, she would come home to him, to roost.

Meanwhile Whiston, a traveller and confidential support of a small firm, hastened about his work, his heart all the while anxious for her, yearning for surety, and kept tense by not getting it.

2

She had been a warehouse girl in Adams's lace factory before she was married. Sam Adams was her employer. He was a bachelor of forty, growing stout, a man well dressed and florid, with a large brown moustache and thin hair. From the rest of his well-groomed, showy appearance, it was evident that his baldness was a chagrin to him. He had a good presence, and some Irish blood in his veins.

His fondness for girls, or the fondness of the girls for him, was notorious. And Elsie, quick, pretty, almost witty little thing – she *seemed* witty, although, when her sayings were repeated, they were entirely trivial – she had a great attraction for him. He would come into the warehouse dressed in a rather sporting reefer coat, of fawn colour, and trousers of fine black and white check, a cap with a big peak and scarlet carnation in his button-hole, to impress her. She was only half impressed. He was too loud for her good taste. Instinctively perceiving this, he sobered down to navy blue. Then a well-built man, florid, with large brown whiskers, smart navy blue suit, fashionable boots, and manly hat, he was the irreproachable. Elsie was impressed.

But meanwhile Whiston was courting her, and she made splendid little gestures, before her bedroom mirror, of the constant-and-true sort.

'True, true till death –'

That was her song. Whiston was made that way, so there was no need to take thought for him.

Every Christmas Sam Adams gave a party at his house, to which he

The Head of the Firm, by Alfred Thomson

invited his superior work-people – not factory hands and labourers but those above. He was a generous man in his way, with a real warm feeling for giving pleasure.

Two years ago Elsie had attended this Christmas-party for the last time. Whiston had accompanied her. At that time he worked for Sam Adams.

She had been very proud of herself, in her close-fitting, full-skirted dress of blue silk. Whiston had called for her. Then she tripped beside him, holding her large cashmere shawl across her breast. He strode with long strides, his trousers handsomely strapped under his boots, and her silk shoes bulging the pockets of his full-skirted overcoat.

They passed through the park gates, and her spirits rose. Above them the Castle Rock loomed grandly in the night, the naked trees stood still and dark in the frost, along the boulevard.

They were rather late. Agitated with anticipation, in the cloakroom she gave up her shawl, donned her silk shoes, and looked at herself in the mirror. The loose bunches of curls on either side her face danced prettily, her mouth smiled.

She hung a moment in the door of the brilliantly lighted room. Many people were moving within the blaze of lamps, under the crystal chandeliers, the full skirts of the women balancing and floating, the side-whiskers and white cravats of the men bowing above. Then she entered the light.

In an instant Sam Adams was coming forward, lifting both his arms in boisterous welcome. There was a constant red laugh on his face.

'Come late, would you,' he shouted, 'like royalty.'

He seized her hands and led her forward. He opened his mouth wide when he spoke, and the effect of the warm, dark opening behind the brown whiskers was disturbing. But she was floating into the throng on his arm. He was very gallant.

'Now then,' he said, taking her card to write down the dances, 'I've got *carte blanche*, haven't I?'

'Mr Whiston doesn't dance,' she said.

'I am a lucky man!' he said, scribbling his initials. 'I was born with an *amourette* in my mouth.'

He wrote on, quietly. She blushed and laughed, not knowing what it meant.

'Why, what is that?' she said.

'It's you, even littler than you are, dressed in little wings,' he said.

'I should have to be pretty small to get in your mouth,' she said.

'You think you're too big, do you?' he said easily.

He handed her her card, with a bow.

'Now I'm set up, my darling, for this evening,' he said.

Then, quick, always at his ease, he looked over the room. She waited in front of him. He was ready. Catching the eye of the band, he nodded. In a moment, the music began. He seemed to relax, giving himself up.

'Now then, Elsie,' he said, with a curious caress in his voice that seemed to lap the outside of her body in a warm glow, delicious. She gave herself up to it. She liked it.

The Dancing Couple

He was an excellent dancer. He seemed to draw her close in to him by some male warmth of attraction, so that she became all soft and pliant to him, flowing to his form, whilst he united her with him and they lapsed along in one movement. She was just carried in a kind of strong, warm flood, her feet moved of themselves, and only the music threw her away from him, threw her back to him, to his clasp, in his strong form moving against her, rhythmically, deliciously.

When it was over, he was pleased and his eyes had a curious gleam which thrilled her and yet had nothing to do with her. Yet it held her. He did not speak to her. He only looked straight into her eyes with a curious, gleaming look that disturbed her fearfully and deliciously. But also there was in his look some of the automatic irony of the *roué*. It left her partly cold. She was not carried away.

She went, driven by an opposite, heavier impulse, to Whiston. He stood looking gloomy, trying to admit that she had a perfect right to enjoy herself apart from him. He received her with a rather grudging kindliness.

'Aren't you going to play whist?' she asked.

'Aye,' he said. 'Directly.'

'I do wish you could dance.'

'Well, I can't,' he said. 'So you enjoy yourself.'

'But I should enjoy it better if I could dance with you.'

'Nay, you're all right,' he said. 'I'm not made that way.'

'Then you ought to be,' she cried.

'Well, it's my fault, not yours. You enjoy yourself,' he bade her. Which she proceeded to do, a little bit irked.

She went with anticipation to the arms of Sam Adams, when the time came to dance with him. It *was* so gratifying, irrespective of the man. And she felt a little grudge against Whiston, soon forgotten when her host was holding her near to him, in a delicious embrace. And she watched his eyes, to meet the gleam in them, which gratified her.

She was getting warmed right through, the glow was penetrating into her, driving away everything else. Only in her heart was a little tightness, like conscience.

When she got a chance, she escaped from the dancing-room to the card-room. There, in a cloud of smoke, she found Whiston playing cribbage. Radiant, roused, animated, she came up to him and greeted him. She was too strong, too vibrant a note in the quiet room. He lifted his head, and a frown knitted his gloomy forehead.

'Are you playing cribbage? Is it exciting? How are you getting on?' she chattered.

He looked at her. None of these questions needed answering, and he did not feel in touch with her. She turned to the cribbage-board.

'Are you red or white?' she asked.

'He's red,' replied the partner.

'Then you're losing,' she said, still to Whiston. And she lifted the red peg from the board. 'One – two – three – four – five – six – seven – eight.

Right up there you ought to jump –'

'Now put it back in its right place,' said Whiston.

'Where was it?' she asked gaily, knowing her transgression. He took the little red peg away from her and stuck it in its hole.

The cards were shuffled.

'What a shame you're losing!' said Elsie.

'You'd better cut for him,' said the partner.

She did so hastily. The cards were dealt. She put her hand on his shoulder, looking at his cards.

'It's good,' she cried, 'isn't it?'

He did not answer, but threw down two cards. It moved him more strongly than was comfortable to have her hand on his shoulder, her curls dangling and touching his ears, whilst she was roused to another man. It made the blood flame over him.

At that moment Sam Adams appeared, florid and boisterous, intoxicated more with himself, with the dancing, than with wine. In his eye the curious impersonal light gleamed.

'I thought I should find you here, Elsie,' he cried boisterously, a disturbing, high note in his voice.

'What made you think so?' she replied, the mischief rousing in her.

The florid, well-built man narrowed his eyes to a smile.

'I should never look for you among the ladies,' he said, with a kind of intimate, animal call to her. He laughed, bowed and offered her his arm.

'Madam, the music waits.'

She went almost helplessly, carried along with him, unwilling, yet delighted.

That dance was an intoxication to her. After the first few steps, she felt herself slipping away from herself. She almost knew she was going, she did not even want to go. Yet she must have chosen to go. She lay in the arm of the steady, close man with whom she was dancing, and she seemed to swim away out of contact with the room, into him. She had passed into another, denser element of him, an essential privacy. The room was all vague around her, like an atmosphere, like under sea, with a flow of ghostly, dumb movements. But she herself was held real against her partner, and it seemed she was connected with him, as if the movements of his body and limbs were her own movements, yet not her own movements – and oh, delicious! He was also given up, oblivious, concentrated, into the dance. His eye was unseeing. Only his large, voluptuous body gave off a subtle activity. His fingers seemed to search

Dance in the Town, by Pierre-Auguste Renoir

into her flesh. Every moment, and every moment, she felt she would give way utterly, and sink molten: the fusion point was coming when she would fuse down into perfect unconsciousness at his feet and knees. But he bore her round the room in the dance, and he seemed to sustain all her body with his limbs, his body, and his warmth seemed to come closer into her, nearer, until it would fuse right through her, and she would be as liquid to him, as an intoxication only.

It was exquisite. When it was over, she was dazed, and was scarcely breathing. She stood with him in the middle of the room as if she were alone in a remote place. He bent over her. She expected his lips on her bare shoulder, and waited. Yet they were not alone, they were not alone. It was cruel.

'T'was good, wasn't it, my darling?' he said to her, low and delighted. There was a strange impersonality about his low, exultant call that appealed to her irresistably. Yet why was she aware of some part shut off in her? She pressed his arm, and he led her towards the door.

She was not aware of what she was doing, only a little grain of resistant trouble was in her. The man, possessed, yet with a superficial presence of mind, made way to the dining-room, as if to give her refreshment, cunningly working to his own escape with her. He was molten hot, filmed over with presence of mind, and bottomed with cold disbelief. In the dining-room was Whiston, carrying coffee to the plain, neglected ladies. Elsie saw him, but felt as if he could not see her. She was beyond his reach and ken. A sort of fusion existed between her and the large man at her side. She ate her custard, but an incomplete fusion all the while sustained and contained her within the being of her employer.

But she was growing cooler. Whiston came up. She looked at him, and saw him with different eyes. She saw his slim, young man's figure real and enduring before her. That was he. But she was in the spell with the other man, fused with him, and she could not be taken away.

'Have you finished your cribbage?' she asked, with hasty evasion of him.

'Yes,' he replied. 'Aren't you getting tired of dancing?'

'Not a bit,' she said.

'Not she,' said Adams heartily. 'No girl with any spirit gets tired of dancing. Have something else, Elsie. Come – sherry. Have a glass of sherry with us, Whiston.'

Whilst they sipped the wine, Adams watched Whiston almost cunningly, to find his advantage.

'We'd better be getting back – there's the music,' he said. 'See the women get something to eat, Whiston, will you, there's a good chap.'

And he began to draw away. Elsie was drifting helplessly with him. But Whiston put himself beside them, and went along with them. In silence they passed through to the dancing-room. There Adams hesitated, and looked round the room. It was as if he could not see.

A man came hurrying forward, claiming Elsie, and Adams went to his other partner. Whiston stood watching during the dance. She was conscious of him standing there observant of her, like a ghost, or a judgment, or a guardian angel. She was also conscious, much more intimately and impersonally, of the body of the other man moving somewhere in the room. She still belonged to him, but a feeling of distraction possessed her, and helplessness. Adams danced on, adhering to Elsie, waiting his time, with the persistence of cynicism.

The dance was over. Adams was detained, Elsie found herself beside Whiston. There was something shapely about him as he sat, about his knees and his distinct figure, that she clung to. It was as if he had enduring form. She put her hand on his knee.

'Are you enjoying yourself?' he asked.

'*Ever so,*' she replied, with a fervent, yet detached tone.

'It's going on for one o'clock,' he said.

'Is it?' she answered. It meant nothing to her.

'Should we be going?' he said.

She was silent. For the first time for an hour or more an inkling of her normal consciousness returned. She resented it.

'What for?' she said.

'I thought you might have had enough,' he said.

A slight soberness came over her, an irritation at being frustrated of her illusion.

'Why?' she said.

'We've been here since nine,' he said.

There was no answer, no reason. It conveyed nothing to her. She sat detached from him. Across the room Sam Adams glanced at her. She sat there exposed for him.

'You don't want to be too free with Sam Adams,' said Whiston cautiously, suffering. 'You know what he is.'

'How, free?' she asked.

'Why – you don't want to have too much to do with him.'

She sat silent. He was forcing her into consciousness of her position.

But he could not get hold of her feelings, to change them. She had a curious, perverse desire that he should not.

'I like him,' she said.

'What do you like in him?' he said, with a hot heart.

'I don't know – but I like him,' she said.

She was immutable. He sat feeling heavy and dulled with rage. He was not clear as to what he felt. He sat there unliving whilst she danced. And she, distracted, lost to herself between the opposing forces of the two men, drifted. Between the dances, Whiston kept near to her. She was scarcely conscious. She glanced repeatedly at her card, to see when she would dance again with Adams, half in desire, half in dread. Sometimes she met his steady, glaucous eye as she passed him in the dance. Sometimes she saw the steadiness of his flank as he danced. And it was always as if she rested on his arm, were borne along, upborne by him, away from herself. And always there was present the other's antagonism. She was divided.

The time came for her to dance with Adams. Oh, the delicious closing of contact with him, of his limbs touching her limbs, his arms supporting her. She seemed to resolve. Whiston had not made himself real to her. He was only a heavy place in her consciousness.

But she breathed heavily, beginning to suffer from the closeness of strain. She was nervous. Adams also was constrained. A tightness, a tension was coming over them all. And he was exasperated, feeling something counteracting physical magnetism, feeling a will stronger with her than his own, intervening in what was becoming a vital necessity to him.

Elsie was almost lost to her own control. As she went forward with him to take her place at the dance, she stooped for her pocket-handkerchief. The music sounded for the quadrilles. Everybody was ready. Adams stood with his body near her, exerting his attraction over her. He was tense and fighting. She stooped for her pocket-handkerchief, and shook it as she rose. It shook out and fell from her hand. With agony, she saw she had taken out a white stocking instead of a handkerchief. For a second it lay on the floor, a twist of white stocking. Then, in an instant, Adams picked it up, with a little, surprised laugh of triumph.

'That'll do for me,' he whispered – seeming to take possession of her. And he stuffed the stocking in his trousers pocket, and quickly offered her his handkerchief.

The dance began. She felt weak and faint, as if her will were turned to water. A heavy sense of loss came over her. She could not help herself any more. But it was peace.

When the dance was over, Adams yielded her up. Whiston came to her.

'What was it as you dropped?' Whiston asked.

'I thought it was my handkerchief – I'd taken a stocking by mistake,' she said, detached and muted.

'And he's got it?'

'Yes.'

'What does he mean by that?'

She lifted her shoulders.

'Are you going to let him keep it?' he asked.

'I don't let him.'

There was a long pause.

'Am I to go and have it out with him?' he asked, his face flushed, his blue eyes going hard with opposition.

'No,' she said, pale.

'Why?'

'No – I don't want you to say anything about it.'

He sat exasperated and nonplussed.

'You'll let him keep it then?' he asked.

She was silent and made no form of answer.

'What do you mean by it?' he said, dark with fury. And he started up.

'No!' she cried. 'Ted!' And she caught hold of him, sharply detaining him.

It made him black with rage.

'Why?' he said.

The something about her mouth was pitiful to him. He did not understand, but he felt she must have her reasons.

'Then I'm not stopping here,' he said. 'Are you coming with me?'

She rose mutely, and they went out of the room. Adams had not noticed.

In a few moments they were in the street.

'What the hell do you mean?' he said, in a black fury.

She went at his side, in silence, neutral.

'That great hog, an' all,' he added.

Then they went a long time in silence through the frozen, deserted darkness of the town. She felt she could not go indoors. They were drawing near her house.

'I don't want to go home,' she suddenly cried in distress and anguish. 'I

A Moonlit Lane with two lovers by a gate, by Atkinson Grimshaw

don't want to go home.'

He looked at her.

'Why don't you?' he said.

'I don't want to go home,' was all she could sob.

71

He heard someone coming.

'Well, we can walk a bit farther,' he said.

She was silent again. They passed out of the town into the fields. He held her by the arm – they could not speak.

'What's a-matter?' he asked at length, puzzled.

She began to cry again.

At last he took her in his arms, to soothe her. She sobbed by herself, almost unaware of him.

'Tell me what's a-matter, Elsie,' he said. 'Tell me what's a-matter – my dear – tell me, then –'

He kissed her wet face, and caressed her. She made no response. He was puzzled and tender and miserable.

At length she became quiet. Then he kissed her, and she put her arms round him, and clung to him very tight, as if for fear and anguish. He held her in his arms, wondering.

'Ted!' she whispered, frantic. 'Ted!'

'What, my love?' he answered, becoming also afraid.

'Be good to me,' she cried. 'Don't be cruel to me.'

'No, my pet,' he said, amazed and grieved. 'Why?'

'Oh, be good to me,' she sobbed.

And he held her very safe, and his heart was white-hot with love for her. His mind was amazed. He could only hold her against his chest that was white-hot with love and belief in her. So she was restored at last.

3

She refused to go back to her work at Adams's any more. Her father had to submit and she sent in her notice – she was not well. Sam Adams was ironical. But he had a curious patience. He did not fight.

In a few weeks, she and Whiston were married. She loved him with a passion and worship, a fierce little abandon of love that moved him to the depths of his being, and gave him a permanent surety and sense of realness in himself. He did not trouble about himself any more: he felt he was fulfilled and now he had only the many things in the world to busy himself about. Whatever troubled him, at the bottom was surety. He had found himself in this love.

They spoke once or twice of the white stocking.

'Ah!' Whiston exclaimed. 'What does it matter?'

He was impatient and angry, and could not bear to consider the matter.

So it was left unresolved.

She was quite happy at first, carried away by her adoration of her husband. Then gradually she got used to him. He always was the ground of her happiness, but she got used to him, as to the air she breathed. He never got used to her in the same way.

Inside of marriage she found her liberty. She was rid of the responsibility of herself. Her husband must look after that. She was free to get what she could out of her time.

So that, when, after some months, she met Sam Adams, she was not quite as unkind to him as she might have been. With a young wife's new and exciting knowledge of men, she perceived he was in love with her, she knew he had always kept an unsatisfied desire for her. And, sportive, she could not help playing a little with this, though she cared not one jot for the man himself.

When Valentine's day came, which was near the first anniversary of her wedding day, there arrived a white stocking with a little amethyst brooch. Luckily Whiston did not see it, so she said nothing of it to him. She had not the faintest intention of having anything to do with Sam Adams, but once a little brooch was in her possession, it was hers, and she did not trouble her head for a moment how she had come by it. She kept it.

Now she had the pearl earrings. They were a more valuable and a more conspicuous present. She would have to ask her mother to give them to her, to explain their presence. She made a little plan in her head. And she was extraordinarily pleased. As for Sam Adams, even if he saw her wearing them, he would not give her away. What fun, if he saw her wearing his earrings! She would pretend she had inherited them from her grandmother, her mother's mother. She laughed to herself as she went downtown in the afternoon, the pretty drops dangling in front of her curls. But she saw no one of importance.

Whiston came home tired and depressed. All day the male in him had been uneasy, and this had fatigued him. She was curiously against him, inclined, as she sometimes was nowadays, to make mock of him and jeer at him and cut him off. He did not understand this, and it angered him deeply. She was uneasy before him.

She knew he was in a state of suppressed irritation. The veins stood out on the backs of his hands, his brow was drawn stiffly. Yet she could not help goading him.

'What did you do wi' that white stocking?' he asked, out of a gloomy

73

silence, his voice strong and brutal.

'I put it in a drawer – why?' she replied flippantly.

'Why didn't you put it on the fire-back?' he said harshly. 'What are you hoarding it up for?'

'I'm not hoarding it up,' she said. 'I've got a pair.'

He relapsed into gloomy silence. She, unable to move him, ran away upstairs, leaving him smoking by the fire. Again she tried on the earrings. Then another little inspiration came to her. She drew on the white stockings, both of them.

Presently she came down in them. Her husband sat immovable and glowering by the fire.

'Look!' she said. 'They'll do beautifully.'

And she picked up her skirts to her knees, and twisted round, looking at her pretty legs in the neat stockings.

He filled with unreasonable rage, and took the pipe from his mouth.

'Don't they look nice?' she said. 'One from last year and one from this, they just do. Save you buying a pair.'

And she looked over her shoulders at her pretty calves, and at the dangling frills of her knickers.

'Put your skirts down and don't make a fool of yourself,' he said.

'Why a fool of myself?' she asked.

And she began to dance slowly round the room, kicking up her feet half reckless, half jeering, in a ballet-dancer's fashion. Almost fearfully, yet in defiance, she kicked up her legs at him, singing as she did so. She resented him.

'You little fool, ha' done with it,' he said. 'And you'll backfire them stockings, I'm telling you.' He was angry. His face flushed dark, he kept his head bent. She ceased to dance.

'I shan't,' she said. 'They'll come in very useful.'

He lifted his head and watched her, with lighted, dangerous eyes.

'You'll put 'em on the fire-back, I tell you,' he said.

It was a war now. She bent forward, in a ballet-dancer's fashion, and put her tongue between her teeth.

'I shan't backfire them stockings,' she sang, repeating his words, 'I shan't, I shan't, I shan't.'

And she danced round the room doing a high kick to the tune of her words. There was a real biting indifference in her behaviour.

'We'll see whether you will or not,' he said, 'trollops! You'd like Sam Adams to know you was wearing 'em, wouldn't you? That's what would

Psyche, by Berthe Morisot

please you.'

'Yes, I'd like him to see how nicely they fit me, he might give me some more then.'

And she looked down at her pretty legs.

He knew somehow that she *would* like Sam Adams to see how pretty her legs looked in the white stockings. It made his anger go deep, almost to hatred.

'Yer nasty trolley,' he cried. 'Put yer petticoats down, and stop being so foul-minded.'

'I'm not foul-minded,' she said. 'My legs are my own. And why shouldn't Sam Adams think they're nice?'

There was a pause. He watched her with eyes glittering to a point.

'Have you been havin' owt to do with him?' he asked.

'I've just spoken to him when I've seen him,' she said. 'He's not as bad as you would make out.'

'Isn't he?' he cried with a certain wakefulness in his voice. 'Them who has anything to do wi' him is too bad for me, I tell you.'

'Why, what are you frightened of him for?' she mocked.

She was rousing all his uncontrollable anger. He sat glowering. Every one of her sentences stirred him up like a red-hot iron. Soon it would be too much. And she was afraid herself; but she was neither conquered nor convinced.

A curious little grin of hate came on his face. He had a long score against her.

'What am I frightened of him for?' he repeated automatically. 'What am I frightened of him for? Why, for you, you stray-running little bitch.'

She flushed. The insult went deep into her, right home.

'Well, if you're so dull –' she said, lowering her eyelids, and speaking coldly, haughtily.

'If I'm so dull I'll break your neck the first word you speak to him,' he said, tense.

'Pf!' she sneered. 'Do you think I'm frightened of you?' She spoke coldly, detached.

She was frightened, for all that, white round the mouth.

His heart was getting hotter.

'You *will* be frightened of me, the next time you have anything to do with him,' he said.

'Do you think *you'd* ever be told – ha!'

Her jeering scorn made him go white-hot, molten. He knew he was incoherent, scarcely responsible for what he might do. Slowly, unseeing, he rose and went out of doors, stifled, moved to kill her.

He stood leaning against the garden fence, unable either to see or hear. Below him, far off, fumed the lights of the town. He stood still, unconscious with a black storm of rage, his face lifted to the night.

Presently, still unconscious of what he was doing, he went indoors again. She stood, a small, stubborn figure with tight-pressed lips and big, sullen, childish eyes, watching him, white with fear. He went heavily across the floor and dropped into his chair.

There was a silence.

'*You're* not going to tell me everything I shall do, and everything I shan't,' she broke out at last.

He lifted his head.

'I tell you *this*,' he said, low and intense. 'Have anything to do with Sam Adams, and I'll break your neck.'

She laughed, shrill and false.

'How I hate your word "break your neck,"' she said, with a grimace of the mouth. 'It sounds so common and beastly. Can't you say something else –'

There was dead silence.

'And besides,' she said, with a queer chirrup of mocking laughter, 'what do you know about anything? He sent me an amethyst brooch and a pair of pearl earrings.'

'He what?' said Whiston, in a suddenly normal voice. His eyes were fixed on her.

'Sent me a pair of pearl earrings, and an amethyst brooch,' she repeated, mechanically, pale to the lips.

And her big, black, childish eyes watched him, fascinated, held in her spell.

He seemed to thrust his face and his eyes forward at her, as he rose slowly and came to her. She watched transfixed in terror. Her throat made a small sound, as she tried to scream.

Then, quick as lightning, the back of his hand struck her with a crash across the mouth, and she was flung back blinded against the wall. The shock shook a queer sound out of her. And then she saw him still coming on, his eyes holding her, his fist drawn back, advancing slowly. At any instant the blow might crash into her.

Mad with terror, she raised her hands with a queer clawing movement to cover her eyes and her temples, opening her mouth in a dumb shriek.

There was no sound. But the sight of her slowly arrested him. He hung before her, looking at her fixedly, as she stood crouched against the wall with open, bleeding mouth, and wide-staring eyes, and two hands clawing over her temples. And his lust to see her bleed, to break her and destroy her, rose from an old source against her. It carried him. He wanted satisfaction.

But he had seen her standing there, a piteous, horrified thing, and he turned his face aside in shame and nausea. He went and sat heavily in his chair, and a curious ease, almost like sleep, came over his brain.

She walked away from the wall towards the fire, dizzy, white to the lips, mechanically wiping her small bleeding mouth. He sat motionless. Then, gradually, her breath began to hiss, she shook, and was sobbing silently, in grief for herself. Without looking, he saw. It made his mad desire to destroy her come back.

At length he lifted his head. His eyes were glowing again, fixed on her.

'And what did he give them you for?' he asked, in a steady, unyielding voice.

Her crying dried up in a second. She also was tense.

'They came as valentines,' she replied, still not subjugated, even if beaten.

'When, today?'

'The pearl earrings today – the amethyst brooch last year.'

'You've had it a year?'

'Yes.'

She felt that now nothing would prevent him if he rose to kill her. She could not prevent him any more. She was yielded up to him. They both trembled in the balance, unconscious.

'What have you had to do with him?' he asked, in a barren voice.

'I've not had anything to do with him,' she quavered.

'You just kept 'em because they were jewellery?' he said.

A weariness came over him. What was the worth of speaking any more of it? He did not care any more. He was dreary and sick.

She began to cry again, but he took no notice. She kept wiping her mouth on her handkerchief. He could see it, the blood-mark. It made him only more sick and tired of the responsibility of it, the violence, the shame.

When she began to move about again, he raised his head once more from his dead motionless position.

'Where are the things?' he said.

'They are upstairs,' she quavered. She knew the passion had gone down in him.

'Bring them down,' he said.

'I won't,' she wept, with rage. 'You're not going to bully me and hit me like that on the mouth.'

And she sobbed again. He looked at her in contempt and compassion and in rising anger.

'Where are they?' he said.

'They're in the little drawer under the looking-glass,' she sobbed.

He went slowly upstairs, struck a match, and found the trinkets. He brought them downstairs in his hand.

'These?' he said, looking at them as they lay in his palm.

She looked at them without answering. She was not interested in them any more.

He looked at the little jewels. They were pretty.

'It's none of their fault,' he said to himself.

And he searched round slowly, persistently, for a box. He tied the things up and addressed them to Sam Adams. Then he went out in his slippers to post the little package.

When he came back she was still sitting crying.

'You'd better go to bed,' he said.

She paid no attention. He sat by the fire. She still cried.

'I'm sleeping down here,' he said. 'Go you to bed.'

In a few moments she lifted her tear-stained, swollen face and looked at him with eyes all forlorn and pathetic. A great flash of anguish went over his body. He went over, slowly, and very gently took her in his hands. She let herself be taken. Then as she lay against his shoulder, she sobbed aloud:

'I never meant – '

'My love – my little love –' he cried, in anguish of spirit, holding her in his arms.

Gloire de Dijon

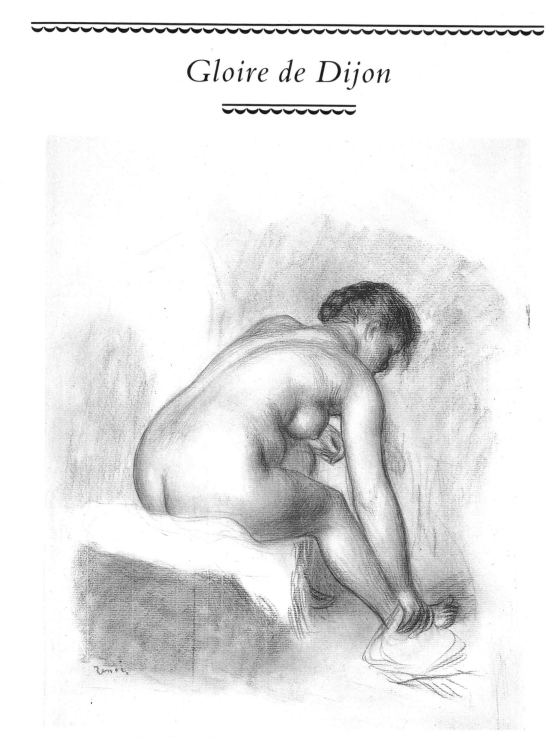

Nude Woman Drying her Foot, by Pierre-Auguste Renoir

In March 1912 Lawrence met his 'woman of a lifetime', Frieda von Richthofen, the wife of his former teacher Ernest Weekley. They eloped to the continent two months later. 'Gloire de Dijon' was written on this 'honeymoon', at Icking in Bavaria, and was published in the exultant volume Look! We Have Come Through! *A letter written at the same time echoes its idyllic tone:*

> The world is wonderful and beautiful and good beyond one's wildest imagination. Never, never, never could one conceive what love is, before-hand, never. Life *can* be great – quite god-like. It *can* be so. God be thanked I have proved it.

Gloire de Dijon

When she rises in the morning
I linger to watch her;
She spreads the bath-cloth underneath the window
And the sunbeams catch her
Glistening white on the shoulders,
While down her sides the mellow
Golden shadow glows as
She stoops to the sponge, and her swung breasts
Sway like full-blown yellow
Gloire de Dijon roses.

She drips herself with water, and her shoulders
Glisten as silver, they crumple up
Like wet and falling roses, and I listen
For the sluicing of their rain-dishevelled petals.
In the window full of sunlight
Concentrates her golden shadow
Fold on fold, until it glows as
Mellow as the glory roses.

The Cathedral

In 1927 Lawrence published a poem called 'Rainbow' in which he declared

> What I see
> when I look at the rainbow
> is one foot in the lap of a woman
> and one in the loins of a man.

The rainbow is the token of God's covenant with Noah; Lawrence employed it as a symbol for the sacrament of marriage. He told his friends the Brewsters:

> For me the rainbow interprets this … the glory shining between every two people which can exist only between them. Each human relationship should be a glorious rainbow.

The visit of the recently-married Anna and Will Brangwen to Lincoln Cathedral is one of the crucial scenes of The Rainbow. *The novel was published in 1915, and banned the same year.*

WHEN HE saw the cathedral in the distance, dark blue lifted watchful in the sky, his heart leapt. It was the sign in heaven, it was the Spirit hovering like a dove, like an eagle over the earth. He turned his glowing, ecstatic face to her, his mouth opened with a strange, ecstatic grin.

'There she is,' he said.

The 'she' irritated her. Why 'she?' It was 'it'. What was the cathedral, a big building, a thing of the past, obsolete, to excite him to such a pitch? She began to stir herself to readiness.

They passed up the steep hill, he eager as a pilgrim arriving at the shrine. As they came near the precincts, the castle on one side and cathedral on the other, his veins seemed to break into fiery blossom, he was transported.

They had passed through the gate, and the great west front was before

Lincoln Cathedral, by Frederick Hines

Holy Silence, by Blair Hughes-Stanton

them, with all its breadth and ornament.

'It is a false front,' he said, looking at the golden stone and the twin towers, and loving them just the same. In a little ecstasy he found himself in the porch, on the brink of the unrevealed. He looked up to the lovely unfolding of the stone. He was to pass within to the perfect womb.

84

Then he pushed open the door, and the great, pillared gloom was before him, in which his soul shuddered and rose from her nest. His soul leapt, soared up into the great church. His body stood still, absorbed by the height. His soul leapt up into the gloom, into possession, it reeled, it swooned with a great escape, it quivered in the womb, in the hush and the gloom of fecundity, like seed of procreation in ecstasy.

She too was overcome with wonder and awe. She followed him in his progress. Here, the twilight was the very essence of life, the coloured darkness was the embryo of all light, and the day. Here, the very first dawn was breaking, the very last sunset sinking, and the immemorial darkness, whereof life's day would blossom and fall away again, re-echoed peace and profound immemorial silence.

Away from time, always outside of time! Between east and west, between dawn and sunset, the church lay like a seed in silence, dark before germination, silenced after death. Containing birth and death, potential with all the noise and transitation of life, the cathedral remained hushed, a great, involved seed, whereof the flower would be radiant life inconceivable, but whose beginning and whose end were the circle of silence. Spanned round with the rainbow, the jewelled gloom folded music upon silence, light upon darkness, fecundity upon death, as a seed folds leaf upon leaf and silence upon the root and the flower, hushing up the secret of all between its parts, the death out of which it fell, the life into which it has dropped, the immortality it involves, and the death it will embrace again.

Here in the church, 'before' and 'after' were folded together, all was contained in oneness. Brangwen came to his consummation. Out of the doors of the womb he had come, putting aside the wings of the womb, and proceeding into the light. Through daylight and day-after-day he had come, knowledge after knowledge, and experience after experience, remembering the darkness of the womb, having prescience of the darkness after death. Then between-while he had pushed open the doors of the cathedral, and entered the twilight of both darknesses, the hush of the two-fold silence, where dawn was sunset, and the beginning and the end were one.

Here, the stone leapt up from the plain earth, leapt up in a manifold, clustered desire each time, up away from the horizontal earth, through twilights and dusk and the whole range of desire, through the swerving, the declination, ah, to the ecstasy, the touch, to the meeting and the consummation, the meeting, the clasp, the close embrace, the neutrality,

Interior of Lincoln Cathedral

the perfect swooning consummation, the timeless ecstasy. There his soul remained, at the apex of the arch, clinched in the timeless ecstasy, consummated.

86

And there was no time nor life nor death, but only this, this timeless consummation, where the thrust from earth met the thrust from earth and the arch was locked on the keystone of ecstasy. This was all, this was everything. Till he came to himself in the world below. Then again he gathered himself together, in transit, every jet of him strained and leaped, leaped clear into the darkness above, to the fecundity and the unique mystery, to the touch, the clasp, the consummation, the climax of eternity, the apex of the arch.

She too was overcome, but silenced rather than tuned to the place. She loved it as a world not quite her own, she resented his transports and ecstasies. His passion in the cathedral at first awed her, then made her angry. After all, there was the sky outside, and in here, in this mysterious half-night, when his soul leapt with the pillars upwards, it was not to the stars and the crystalline dark space, but to meet and clasp with the answering impulse of leaping stone, there in the dusk and secrecy of the roof. The far-off clinching and mating of arches, the leap and thrust of the stone, carrying a great roof overhead, awed and silenced her.

But yet – she remembered that the open sky was no blue vault, no dark dome hung with many twinkling lamps, but a space where stars were wheeling in freedom, with freedom above them always higher.

The cathedral roused her too. But she would never consent to the knitting of all the leaping stone in a great roof that closed her in, and beyond which there was nothing, nothing, it was the ultimate confine. His soul would have liked it to be so: here, here is all, complete, eternal: motion, meeting, ecstasy, and no illusion of time, of night and day passing by, but only perfectly proportioned space and movement clinching and renewing, and passion surging its way in great waves to the altar, recurrence of ecstasy.

Her soul too was carried forward to the altar, to the threshold of Eternity, in reverence and fear and joy. But ever she hung back in the transit, mistrusting the culmination of the altar. She was not to be flung forward on the lift and lift of passionate flights, to be cast at last upon the altar steps as upon the shore of the unknown. There was a great joy and a verity in it. But even in the dazed swoon of the cathedral, she claimed another right. The altar was barren, its lights gone out. God burned no more in that bush. It was dead matter lying there. She claimed the right to freedom above her, higher than the roof. She had always a sense of being roofed in.

So that she caught at little things, which saved her from being swept forward headlong in the tide of passion that leaps on into the Infinite in a great mass, triumphant and flinging its own course. She wanted to get out of this fixed, leaping, forward-travelling movement, to rise from it as a bird rises with wet, limp feet from the sea, to lift herself as a bird lifts its breast and thrusts its body from the pulse and heave of a sea that bears it forward to an unwilling conclusion, tear herself away like a bird on wings, and in the open space where there is clarity, rise up above the fixed, surcharged motion, a separate speck that hangs suspended, moves this way and that, seeing and answering before it sinks again, having chosen or found the direction in which it shall be carried forward.

And it was as if she must grasp at something, as if her wings were too weak to lift her straight off the heaving motion. So she caught sight of the wicked, odd little faces carved in stone, and she stood before them arrested.

These sly little faces peeped out of the grand tide of the cathedral like something that knew better. They knew quite well, these little imps that retorted on a man's own illusion, that the cathedral was not absolute. They winked and leered, giving suggestion of the many things that had been left out of the great concept of the church. 'However much there is inside here, there's a good deal they haven't got in,' the little faces mocked.

Apart from the lift and spring of the great impulse towards the altar, these little faces had separate wills, separate motions, separate knowledge, which rippled back in defiance of the tide, and laughed in triumph of their own very littleness.

'Oh, look!' cried Anna, 'Oh, look, how adorable, the faces! Look at her.'

Brangwen looked unwillingly. This was the voice of the serpent in his Eden. She pointed him to a plump, sly, malicious little face carved in stone.

'He knew her, the man who carved her,' said Anna. 'I'm sure she was his wife.'

'It isn't a woman at all, it's a man,' said Brangwen curtly.

'Do you think so? – No! That isn't a man. That is no man's face.'

Her voice sounded rather jeering. He laughed shortly, and went on. But she would not go forward with him. She loitered about the carvings. And he could not go forward without her. He waited impatient of this counter-action. She was spoiling his passionate intercourse with the cathedral. His brows began to gather.

Will and Anna Brangwen's Cottage at Cossethay

'I have finished my Rainbow', by D.H. Lawrence

'Oh this is good!' she cried again. 'Here is the same woman – look! – only he's made her cross! Isn't it lovely! Hasn't he made her hideous to a degree?' She laughed with pleasure. 'Didn't he hate her? He must have been a nice man! Look at her – isn't it awfully good – just like a shrewish woman. He must have enjoyed putting her in like that. He got his own back on her, didn't he?'

'It's a man's face, no woman's at all – a monk's – clean shaven,' he said.

She laughed with a Pouf! of laughter.

'You hate to think he put his wife in your cathedral, don't you?' she mocked, with a tinkle of profane laughter. And she laughed with malicious triumph.

She had got free from the cathedral, she had even destroyed the passion he had. She was glad. He was bitterly angry. Strive as he would, he could not keep the cathedral wonderful to him. He was disillusioned. That which had been his absolute, containing all heaven and earth, was become to him as to her, a shapely heap of dead matter – but dead, dead.

His mouth was full of ash, his soul was furious. He hated her for having destroyed another of his vital illusions. Soon he would be stark, stark, without one place wherein to stand, without one belief in which to rest.

Yet somewhere in him he responded more deeply to the sly little face that knew better, than he had done before to the perfect surge of his cathedral.

Architectural study,
by S.R. Badmin

The Rainbow

This short poem forms part of a sequence of meditations on the nature of God and the mystery of creation, in Lawrence's Last Poems. God, Lawrence writes, 'is the great urge that has not yet found a body'.

The Rainbow

Even the rainbow has a body
made of the drizzling rain
and is an architecture of glistening atoms
built up, built up
yet you can't lay your hand on it,
nay, nor even your mind.

Detail from The Blind Girl, *by John Everett Millais*

The Water-Party

The water-party in this chapter of Women in Love, *the sequel to* The Rainbow, *ends with tragedy: a double drowning. It was a real incident from the life of a local notable in Lawrence's childhood; Lawrence may even have been present. This man, Major Thomas Philip Barber, provided an outer casing for the figure of Gerald, though by the time Lawrence had cast his mass of material into its final form, Gerald's character owed much to John Middleton Murry, as Gudrun's did to Katherine Mansfield. Lawrence nearly always based his characters on friends and acquaintances, often with disastrous results for the friendship. The literary hostess Ottoline Morrell, who had been generous and kind to Lawrence, held up publication of* Women in Love *for several years in revulsion at the spiteful portrait of her as Hermione Roddice.*

EVERY YEAR Mr Crich gave a more or less public water-party on the lake. There was a little pleasure-launch on Willey Water and several rowing boats, and guests could take tea either in the marquee that was set up in the grounds of the house, or they could picnic in the shade of the great walnut-tree at the boat-house by the lake. This year the staff of the Grammar School was invited, along with the chief officials of the firm. Gerald and the younger Criches did not care for this party, but it had become customary now, and it pleased the father, as being the only occasion when he could gather some people of the district together in festivity with him. For he loved to give pleasures to his dependents and to those poorer than himself. But his children preferred the company of their own equals in wealth. They hated their inferiors' humility or gratitude or awkwardness.

Nevertheless they were willing to attend at this festival, as they had done almost since they were children, the more so, as they all felt a little guilty now, and unwilling to thwart their father any more, since he was so ill in health. Therefore, quite cheerfully Laura prepared to take her mother's place as hostess, and Gerald assumed responsibility for the amusements on the water.

Birkin had written to Ursula saying he expected to see her at the party, and Gudrun, although she scorned the patronage of the Criches, would nevertheless accompany her mother and father if the weather were fine.

The day came blue and full of sunshine, with little wafts of wind. The sisters both wore dresses of white crepe, and hats of soft grass. But Gudrun had a sash of brilliant black and pink and yellow colour wound broadly round her waist, and she had pink silk stockings, and black and pink and yellow decoration on the brim of her hat, weighing it down a little. She carried also a yellow silk coat over her arm, so that she looked remarkable, like a painting from the Salon. Her appearance was a sore trial to her father, who said angrily:

'Don't you think you might as well get yourself up for a Christmas cracker, an' ha' done with it?'

But Gudrun looked handsome and brilliant, and she wore her clothes in pure defiance. When people stared at her, and giggled after her, she made a point of saying loudly, to Ursula:

'Regarde, regarde ces gens-là. Ne sont-ils pas des hiboux incroyables?' And with the words of French in her mouth, she would look over her shoulder at the giggling party.

'No, really, it's impossible!' Ursula would reply distinctly. And so the two girls took it out on their universal enemy. But their father became more and more enraged.

Ursula was snowy white, save that her hat was pink, and entirely without trimming, and her shoes were dark red, and she carried an orange-coloured coat. And in this guise they were walking all the way to Shortlands, their father and mother going in front.

They were laughing at their mother, who, dressed in a summer material of black and purple stripes, and wearing a hat of purple straw, was setting forth with much more of the shyness and trepidation of a young girl than her daughters ever felt, walking demurely beside her husband, who, as usual, looked rather crumpled in his best suit, as if he were the father of a young family and had been holding the baby whilst his wife got dressed.

'Look at the young couple in front,' said Gudrun calmly. Ursula looked at her mother and father, and was suddenly seized with uncontrollable laughter. The two girls stood in the road and laughed till the tears ran down their faces, as they caught sight again of the shy, unworldly couple of their parents going on ahead.

'We are roaring at you, Mother,' called Ursula, helplessly following after her parents.

Mrs Brangwen turned round with a slightly puzzled, exasperated look. 'Oh, indeed!' she said. 'What is there so very funny about *me*, I should like to know?'

She could not understand that there could be anything amiss with her appearance. She had a perfect calm sufficiency, an easy indifference to any criticism whatsoever, as if she were beyond it. Her clothes were always rather odd, and as a rule slip-shod, yet she wore them with a perfect ease and satisfaction. Whatever she had on, so long as she was barely tidy, she was right, beyond remark; such an aristocrat she was by instinct.

'You look so stately, like a country Baroness,' said Ursula, laughing with a little tenderness at her mother's naive puzzled air.

'*Just* like a country Baroness!' chimed in Gudrun. Now the mother's natural hauteur became self-conscious, and the girls shrieked again.

'Go home, you pair of idiots, great giggling idiots!' cried the father, inflamed with irritation.

'Mm-m-er!' booed Ursula, pulling a face at his crossness.

The yellow lights danced in his eyes, he leaned forward in real rage.

'Don't be so silly as to take any notice of the great gabies,' said Mrs Brangwen, turning on her way.

'I'll see if I'm going to be followed by a pair of giggling yelling jackanapes,' he cried vengefully.

The girls stood still, laughing helplessly at his fury, upon the path beside the hedge.

'Why you're as silly as they are, to take any notice,' said Mrs Brangwen, also becoming angry now he was really enraged.

'There are some people coming, Father,' cried Ursula, with mocking warning. He glanced round quickly, and went on to join his wife, walking stiff with rage. And the girls followed, weak with laughter.

When the people had passed by, Brangwen cried in a loud, stupid voice:

'I'm going back home if there's any more of this. I'm damned if I'm going to be made a fool of in this fashion, in the public road.'

He was really out of temper. At the sound of his blind, vindictive voice, the laughter suddenly left the girls, and their hearts contracted with contempt. They hated his words 'in the public road'. What did they care for the public road? – but Gudrun was conciliatory.

'But we weren't laughing to *hurt* you,' she cried, with an uncouth gentleness which made her parents uncomfortable. 'We were laughing because we're fond of you.'

'We'll walk on in front, if they are *so* touchy,' said Ursula, angry. And in this wise they arrived at Willey Water. The lake was blue and fair, the meadows sloped down in sunshine on one side, the thick dark woods dropped steeply on the other. The little pleasure-launch was fussing out from the shore, twanging its music, crowded with people, flapping its paddles. Near the boat-house was a throng of gaily-dressed persons, small in the distance. And on the high-road, some of the common people were standing along the hedge, looking at the festivity beyond, enviously, like souls not admitted to paradise.

'My eye!' said Gudrun, *sotto voce*, looking at the motley of guests, 'there's a pretty crowd if you like! Imagine yourself in the midst of that, my dear.'

Gudrun's apprehensive horror of people in the mass unnerved Ursula. 'It looks rather awful,' she said anxiously.

'Imagine what they'll be like – *imagine*!' said Gudrun, still in that unnerving, subdued voice. Yet she advanced determinedly.

'I suppose we can get away from them,' said Ursula anxiously.

'We're in a pretty fix if we can't,' said Gudrun. Her extreme, ironic loathing and apprehension was very trying to Ursula.

'We needn't stay,' she said.

'I certainly shan't stay five minutes among that little lot,' said Gudrun. They advanced nearer, till they saw policemen at the gates.

'Policemen to keep you in, too!' said Gudrun. 'My word, this is a beautiful affair.'

'We'd better look after father and mother,' said Ursula, anxiously.

'Mother's *perfectly* capable of getting through this little celebration,' said Gudrun with some contempt.

But Ursula knew that her father felt uncouth and angry and unhappy, so she was far from her ease. They waited outside the gate until their parents came up. The tall, thin man in his crumpled clothes, was unnerved and irritable as a boy, finding himself on the brink of this social function. He did not feel a gentleman, he did not feel anything except pure exasperation.

Ursula took her place at his side, they gave their tickets to the

Lunch at Villeneuve-sur-Yonne, by Edouard Vuillard

policeman, and passed in on to the grass, four abreast; the tall, hot, ruddy-dark man with his narrow, boyish brow drawn with irritation, the fresh-faced easy woman, perfectly collected, though her hair was slipping on one side, then Gudrun, her eyes round and dark and staring, her

Lunch at Villeneuve-sur-Yonne, by Edouard Vuillard

full soft face impassive, almost sulky, so that she seemed to be backing away in antagonism even whilst she was advancing; and then Ursula, with the odd, brilliant, dazzled look on her face, that always came when she was in some false situation.

explore that coast?' She pointed to a grove on the hillock of the meadow-side, near the shore, half way down the lake. 'That looks perfectly lovely. We might even bathe. Isn't it beautiful in this light! – Really, it's like one of the reaches of the Nile – as one imagines the Nile.'

Gerald smiled at her factitious enthusiasm for the distant spot.

'You're sure it's far enough off?' he asked ironically, adding at once: 'Yes, you might go there, if we could get a boat. They seem to be all out.'

He looked round the lake and counted the rowing boats on its surface.

'How lovely it would be!' cried Ursula wistfully.

'And don't you want tea?' he said.

'Oh,' said Gudrun, 'we could just drink a cup, and be off.'

He looked from one to the other, smiling. He was somewhat offended – yet sporting.

'Can you manage a boat pretty well?' he asked.

'Yes,' replied Gudrun, coldly, 'pretty well.'

'Oh yes,' cried Ursula. 'We can both of us row like water-spiders.'

'You can? – There's a light little canoe of mine, that I didn't take out for fear somebody should drown themselves. Do you think you'd be safe in that?

'Oh perfectly,' said Gudrun.

'What an angel!' cried Ursula.

'Don't, for *my* sake, have an accident – because I'm responsible for the water.'

'Sure,' pledged Gudrun.

'Besides, we can both swim quite well,' said Ursula.

'Well – then, I'll get them to put you up a tea basket, and you can picnic all to yourselves, – that's the idea, isn't it?'

'How fearfully good! How frightfully nice if you could!' cried Gudrun warmly, her colour flushing up again. It made the blood stir in his veins, the subtle way she turned to him and infused her gratitude into his body.

'Where's Birkin?' he said, his eyes twinkling. 'He might help me to get it down.'

'But what about your hand! Isn't it hurt!' asked Gudrun, rather muted, as if avoiding the intimacy. This was the first time the hurt had been mentioned. The curious way she skirted round the subject sent a new, subtle caress through his veins. He took his hand out of his pocket. It was bandaged. He looked at it, then put it in his pocket again. Gudrun quivered at the sight of the wrapped up paw.

'Oh, I can manage with one hand. The canoe is as light as a feather,' he said. 'There's Rupert! – Rupert!'

Birkin turned from his social duties and came towards them.

'What have you done to it!' asked Ursula, who had been aching to put the question for the last half hour.

'To my hand?' said Gerald. 'I trapped it in some machinery.'

'Ugh!' said Ursula. 'And did it hurt much?'

'Yes,' he said. 'It did at the time. It's getting better now. It crushed the fingers.

'Oh,' cried Ursula, as if in pain, 'I hate people who hurt themselves. I can *feel* it.' And she shook her hand.

'What do you want?' said Birkin.

The two men carried down the slim brown boat, and set it on the water.

'You're quite sure you'll be safe in it?' Gerald said.

'Quite sure,' said Gudrun. 'I wouldn't be so mean as to take it, if there was the slightest doubt. But I've had a canoe at Arundel, and I assure you I'm perfectly safe.'

So saying, and having given her word like a man, she and Ursula entered the frail craft, and pushed gently off. The two men stood watching them. Gudrun was paddling. She knew the men were watching her, and it made her slow and rather clumsy. The colour flew in her face like a flag.

'Thanks awfully,' she called back to him, from the water, as the boat slid away. 'It's lovely – like sitting in a leaf.'

He laughed at the fancy. Her voice was shrill and strange, calling from the distance. He watched her as she paddled away. There was something childlike about her, trustful and deferential, like a child. He watched her all the while, as she rowed. And to Gudrun it was a real delight, in make-belief, to be the childlike, clinging woman to the man who stood there on the quay, so goodlooking and efficient in his white clothes, and moreover the most important man she knew at the moment. She did not take any notice of the wavering, indistinct, lambent Birkin, who stood at his side. One figure at a time occupied the field of her attention.

The boat rustled lightly along the water. They passed the bathers whose striped tents stood between the willows of the meadow's edge, and drew along the open shore, past the meadow that sloped golden in the light of the already late afternoon. Other boats were stealing under

OVERLEAF: *A Summer's Day, by Berthe Morisot*

the wooded shore opposite, they could hear people's laughter and voices. But Gudrun rowed on towards the clump of trees that balanced perfect in the distance, in the golden light.

The sisters found a little place where a tiny stream flowed into the lake, with reeds and flowery marsh of pink willow herb, and a gravelly bank to the side. Here they ran delicately ashore, with their frail boat, the two girls took off their shoes and stockings and went through the water's edge to the grass. The tiny ripples of the lake were warm and clear, they lifted their boat on to the bank, and looked round with joy. They were quite alone in a foresaken little stream-mouth, and on the knoll just behind was the clump of trees.

'We will bathe just for a moment,' said Ursula, 'and then we'll have tea.'

They looked round. Nobody could notice them, or could come up in time to see them. In less than a minute Ursula had thrown off her clothes and had slipped naked into the water, and was swimming out. Quickly, Gudrun joined her. They swam silently and blissfully for a few minutes, circling round their little stream-mouth. Then they slipped ashore and ran into the grove again, like nymphs.

'How lovely it is to be free,' said Ursula, running swiftly here and there between the tree trunks, quite naked, her hair flowing loose. The grove was of beech-trees, big and splendid, a steel-grey scaffolding of trunks and boughs, with level sprays of strong green here and there, whilst through the northern side the distance glimmered open as through a window.

When they had run and danced themselves dry, the girls quickly dressed and sat down to the fragrant tea. They sat on the northern side of the grove, in the yellow sunshine facing the slope of the grassy hill, alone in a little wild world of their own. The tea was hot and aromatic, there were delicious little sandwiches of cucumber and of caviare, and winy cakes.

'Are you happy, Prune?' cried Ursula in delight, looking at her sister.

'Ursula, I'm perfectly happy,' replied Gudrun gravely, looking at the westering sun.

'So am I.'

When they were together, doing the things they enjoyed, the two sisters were quite complete in a perfect world of their own. And this was one of the perfect moments of freedom and delight, such as children alone know, when all seems a perfect and blissful adventure.

A Bather, by Pierre-Auguste Renoir

When they had finished tea, the two girls sat on, silent and serene. Then Ursula, who had a beautiful strong voice, began to sing to herself, softly: 'Annchen von Tharau.' Gudrun listened, as she sat beneath the trees, and the yearning came into her heart. Ursula seemed so peaceful and sufficient unto herself, sitting there unconsciously crooning her song, strong and unquestioned at the centre of her own universe. And Gudrun felt herself outside. Always, this desolating, agonised feeling, that she was outside of life, an onlooker, whilst Ursula was a partaker, caused Gudrun to suffer from a sense of her own negation, and made her, that she must always demand the other to be aware of her, to be in connection with her.

'Do you mind if I do Dalcroze to that tune, Hurtler?' she asked in a curious muted tone, scarce moving her lips.

'What did you say?' asked Ursula, looking up in peaceful surprise.

'Will you sing while I do Dalcroze?' said Gudrun, suffering at having to repeat herself.

Ursula thought a moment, gathering her straying wits together.

'While you do –?' she asked vaguely.

'Dalcroze movements,' said Gudrun, suffering tortures of self-consciousness, even because of her sister.

'Oh, Dalcroze! I couldn't catch the name. *Do* – I should love to see you,' cried Ursula, with childish surprised brightness. 'What shall I sing?'

'Sing anything you like, and I'll take the rhythm from it.'

But Ursula could not for her life think of anything to sing. However, she suddenly began, in a laughing, teasing voice:

'My love – is a high-born lady –'

Gudrun, looking as if some invisible chain weighed on her hands and feet, began slowly to dance in the eurythmic manner, pulsing and fluttering rhythmically with her feet, making slow, regular gestures with her hands and arms, now spreading her arms wide, now raising them above her head, now flinging them softly apart, and lifting her face, her feet all the time beating and running to the measure of the song, as if it were some strange incantation, her white, rapt form drifting here and there in a strange impulsive rhapsody, seeming to be lifted on a breeze of incantation, shuddering with strange little runs. Ursula sat on the grass, her mouth open in her singing, her eyes laughing as if she thought it was a great joke, but a yellow light flashing up in them, as she caught some of the unconscious ritualistic suggestion of the complex shuddering and waving and drifting of her sister's white form, that was clutched in pure, mindless, tossing rhythm, and a will set powerful in a kind of hypnotic influence.

Mrs Barnard and Miss Williams, by John Singer Sargent

'My love is a high-born lady – She is-s-s – rather dark than shady –' rang out Ursula's laughing, satiric song, and quicker, fiercer went Gudrun in the dance, stamping as if she were trying to throw off some bond, flinging her hands suddenly and stamping again, then rushing with face uplifted and throat full and beautiful, and eyes half closed, sightless. The sun was low and yellow, sinking down, and in the sky floated a thin, ineffectual moon.

Ursula was quite absorbed in her song, when suddenly Gudrun stopped and said mildly, ironically:

'Ursula?'

'Yes?' said Ursula, opening her eyes out of the trance.

Gudrun was standing still and pointing, a mocking smile on her face, towards the side.

'Ugh!' cried Ursula in sudden panic, starting to her feet.

'They're quite all right,' rang out Gudrun's sardonic voice.

On the left stood a little cluster of Highland cattle, vividly coloured and fleecy in the evening light, their horns branching into the sky, pushing forward their muzzles inquisitively, to know what it was all about. Their eyes glittered through their tangle of hair, their naked nostrils were full of shadow.

'Won't they do anything?' cried Ursula in fear.

Gudrun, who was usually frightened of cattle, now shook her head in a queer, half-doubtful, half-sardonic motion, a faint smile round her mouth.

'Don't they look charming, Ursula?' cried Gudrun, in a high, strident voice, something like the scream of a sea-gull.

'Charming,' cried Ursula in trepidation. 'But won't they do anything to us?'

Again Gudrun looked back at her sister with an enigmatic smile, and shook her head.

'I'm sure they won't,' she said, as if she had to convince herself also, and yet, as if she were confident of some secret power in herself, and had to put it to the test. 'Sit down and sing again,' she called in her high, strident voice.

'I'm frightened,' cried Ursula, in a pathetic voice, watching the group of sturdy short cattle, that stood with their knees planted, and watched with their dark, wicked eyes, through the matted fringe of their hair. Nevertheless, she sank down again, in her former posture.

'They are quite safe,' came Gudrun's high call. 'Sing something, you've only to sing something.'

It was evident she had a strange passion to dance before the sturdy, handsome cattle.

Ursula began to sing, in a false quavering voice:

'It's a long way to Tipperary ...'

She sounded purely anxious. Nevertheless Gudrun, with her arms outspread and her face uplifted, went in a strange palpitating dance towards the cattle, lifting her body towards them as if in a spell, her feet pulsing as if in some little frenzy of unconscious sensation, her arms, her wrists, her hands stretching and heaving and falling and reaching and reaching and falling, her breasts lifted and shaken towards the cattle, her throat exposed as in some voluptuous ecstasy towards them, whilst she drifted imperceptibly nearer, an uncanny white figure, towards them, carried away in its own rapt trance, ebbing in strange fluctuations upon the cattle, that waited, and ducked their heads a little in sudden contraction from her, watching all the time as if hypnotised, their bare horns branching in the clear light, as the white figure of the woman ebbed upon them, in the slow, hypnotising convulsion of the dance. She could feel them just in front of her, it was as if she had the electric pulse from their breasts running into her hands. Soon she would touch them, actually touch them. A terrible shiver of fear and pleasure went through her. And all the while, Ursula, spell-bound, kept up her high-pitched thin, irrelevant song, which pierced the fading evening like an incantation.

Gudrun could hear the cattle breathing heavily with helpless fear and fascination. Oh, they were brave little beasts, these wild Scotch bullocks, wild and fleccy. Suddenly one of them snorted, ducked its head and backed.

'Hue! Hi-eee!' came a sudden loud shout from the edge of the grove. The cattle broke and fell back quite spontaneously, went running up the hill, their fleece waving like fire to their motion. Gudrun stood suspended out on the grass, Ursula rose to her feet.

It was Gerald and Birkin come to find them, and Gerald had cried out to frighten off the cattle.

'What do you think you're doing?' he now called, in a high, wondering vexed voice.

'Why have you come?' came back Gudrun's strident cry of anger.

'What do you think you were doing?' Gerald repeated, automatically.

'We were doing eurythmics,' laughed Ursula, in a shaken voice.

Gudrun stood aloof, looking at them with large dark eyes of resentment, suspended for a few moments. Then she walked away up the hill,

OVERLEAF: *The Parasol, by Arthur Hacker*

after the cattle, which had gathered in a little, spell-bound cluster higher up.

'Where are you going?' Gerald called after her. And he followed her up the hillside. The sun had gone behind the hill, and shadows were clinging to the earth, the sky above was full of travelling light.

'A poor song for a dance,' said Birkin to Ursula, standing before her with a sardonic, flickering laugh on his face. And in another second, he was singing softly to himself, and dancing a grotesque step-dance in front of her, his limbs and body shaking loose, his face flickering palely, a constant thing, whilst his feet beat a rapid mocking tattoo, and his body seemed to hang all loose and quaking in between, like a shadow.

'I think we've all gone mad,' she said, laughing rather frightened.

'Pity we aren't madder,' he answered, as he kept up the incessant shaking dance. Then suddenly he leaped up to her and kissed her fingers lightly, putting his face to hers and looking into her eyes with a pale grin. She stepped back, affronted.

'Offended –?' he asked ironically, suddenly going quite still and reserved again. 'I thought you liked the light fantastic.'

'Not like that,' she said, confused and bewildered, almost affronted. Yet somewhere inside her she was fascinated by the sight of his loose, vibrating body, perfectly abandoned to its own dropping and swinging, and by the pallid, sardonic smiling face above. Yet automatically, she stiffened herself away and disapproved. It seemed almost an obscenity, in a man who talked as a rule so very seriously.

'Why not like that?' he mocked. And immediately he dropped again into the incredibly rapid, slack-waggling dance, watching her malevolently. And moving in the rapid stationary dance, he came a little nearer, and reached forward with an incredibly mocking, satiric gleam on his face, and would have kissed her again, had she not started back.

'No, don't!' she cried, really afraid.

'Cordelia after all,' he said satirically. She was stung, as if this were an insult. She knew he intended it as such, and it bewildered her.

'And you,' she cried in retort, 'why do you always take your soul in your mouth, so frightfully full!'

'So that I can spit it out the more readily,' he said, pleased by his own retort.

Gerald Crich, his face narrowing to an intent gleam, followed up the hill with quick strides, straight after Gudrun. The cattle stood with their noses together on the brow of a slope, watching the scene below, the men in white hovering about the white forms of the woman, watching above all Gudrun, who was advancing slowly towards them. She stood a moment, glancing back at Gerald, and then at the cattle.

Then in a sudden motion, she lifted her arms and rushed sheer upon the long-horned bullocks, in shuddering irregular runs, pausing for a second and looking at them, then lifting her hands and running forward with a flash, till they ceased pawing the ground, and gave way, snorting with terror, lifting their heads from the ground and flinging themselves away, galloping off into the evening, becoming tiny in the distance, and still not stopping.

Gudrun remained staring after them, with a mask-like defiant face.

'Why do you want to drive them mad?' asked Gerald, coming up with her.

She took no notice of him, only averted her face from him.

'It's not safe, you know,' he persisted. 'They're nasty, when they do turn.'

'Turn where? Turn away?' she mocked loudly.

'No,' he said, 'turn against you.'

'Against *me*?' she mocked.

He could make nothing of this.

'Anyway, they gored one of the farmer's cows to death, the other day,' he said.

'What do I care?' she said.

'I cared though,' he replied, 'seeing that they're my cattle.'

'How are they yours! You haven't swallowed them. Give me one of them now,' she said, holding out her hand.

'You know where they are,' he said, pointing over the hill. 'You can have one if you'd like it sent to you later on.'

She looked at him inscrutably.

'You think I'm afraid of you and your cattle, don't you?' she asked.

His eyes narrowed dangerously. There was a faint domineering smile on his face.

'Why should I think that?' he said.

She was watching him all the time with her dark, dilated, inchoate eyes. She leaned forward and swung round her arm, catching him a blow on the face with the back of her hand.

'That's why,' she said.

And she felt in her soul an unconquerable lust for deep brutality against him. She shut off the fear and dismay that filled her conscious mind. She wanted to do as she did, she was not going to be afraid.

He recoiled from the heavy blow across the face. He became deadly pale, and a dangerous flame darkened his eyes. For some seconds he could not speak, his lungs were so suffused with blood, his heart stretched almost to bursting with a great rush of ungovernable rage. It was as if some reservoir of black anger had burst within him, and swamped him.

'You have struck the first blow,' he said at last, forcing the words from his lungs, in a voice so soft and low, it sounded like a dream within her, not spoken in the outer air.

'And I shall strike the last,' she retorted involuntarily, with confident assurance. He was silent, he did not contradict her,

She stood negligently, staring away from him, into the distance. On the edge of her consciousness the question was asking itself, automatically:

'Why *are* you behaving in this *impossible* and ridiculous fashion?' But she was sullen, she half shoved the question out of herself. She could not get it clean away, so she felt self-conscious.

Gerald, very pale, was watching her closely. His eyes were lit up with intent lights, absorbed and gleaming. She turned suddenly on him.

'It's you who make me behave like this, you know,' she said, almost suggestive.

'I? How?' he said.

But she turned away, and set off towards the lake. Below, on the water, lanterns were coming alight, faint ghosts of warm flame floating in the pallor of the first twilight. The earth was spread with darkness, like lacquer, overhead was a pale sky, all primrose, and the lake was pale as milk in one part. Away at the landing stage, tiniest points of coloured rays were stringing themselves in the dusk. The launch was being illuminated. All round, shadow was gathering from the trees.

Gerald, white like a presence in his summer clothes, was following down the open grassy slope. Gudrun waited for him to come up. Then she softly put out her hand and touched him, saying softly:

'Don't be angry with me.'

A flame flew over him, and he was unconscious. Yet he stammered:

'I'm not angry with you. I'm in love with you.'

His mind was gone, he grasped for sufficient mechanical control to save himself. She laughed a silvery little mockery, yet intolerably caressive.

'That's one way of putting it,' she said.

The terrible swooning burden on his mind, the awful swooning, the loss of all his control was too much for him. He grasped her arm in his one hand, as if his hand were iron.

'It's all right, then, is it?' he said, holding her arrested.

She looked at the face with the fixed eyes, set before her, and her blood ran cold.

'Yes, it's all right,' she said softly, as if drugged, her voice crooning and witch-like.

He walked on beside her, a striding, mindless body. But he recovered a little as he went. He suffered badly. He had killed his brother when a boy, and was set apart, like Cain.

They found Birkin and Ursula sitting together by the boats, talking and laughing. Birkin had been teasing Ursula.

'Do you smell this little marsh?' he said, sniffing the air. He was very sensitive to scents, and quick in understanding them.

'It's rather nice,' she said.

'No,' he replied, 'alarming.'

'Why alarming?' she laughed.

'It seethes and seethes, a river of darkness,' he said, 'putting forth lilies and snakes, and the ignis fatuus, and rolling all the time onward. That's what we never take into account – that it rolls onwards.'

'What does?

'The other river, the black river. We always consider the silver river of life, rolling on and quickening all the world to a brightness, on and on to heaven, flowing into a bright eternal sea, a heaven of angels thronging. – But the other is our real reality –'

'But what other? I don't see any other,' said Ursula.

'It is your reality, nevertheless,' he said, 'the dark river of dissolution. – You see it rolls in us just as the other rolls – the black river of corruption. And our flowers are of this – our sea-born Aphrodite, all our realities, nowadays.'

'You mean that Aphrodite is really deathly?' asked Ursula.

'I mean she is the flowering mystery of the death-process, yes,' he replied. 'When the stream of synthetic creation lapses, we find ourselves part of the inverse process, the flood of destructive creation. Aphrodite is born in the first spasm of universal dissolution – then the snakes and swans and lotus – marsh-flowers – and Gudrun and Gerald – born in the process of destructive creation.'

'And you and me – ? she asked.

'Probably,' he replied. 'In part, certainly. Whether we are that, in toto, I don't yet know.'

'You mean we are flowers of dissolution – fleurs du mal? – I don't feel as if I were,' she protested.

He was silent for a time.

'I don't feel as if we were, *altogether*,' he replied. 'Some people are pure flowers of dark corruption – lilies. But there ought to be some roses, warm and flamy. –You know, Herakleitos says "a dry soul is best". I know so well what that means. Do you?'

'I'm not sure,' Ursula replied. 'But what if people *are* all flowers of dissolution – when they're flowers at all – what difference does it make?'

'No difference – and all the difference. Dissolution rolls on, just as production does,' he said. 'It is a progressive process – and it ends in universal nothing – the end of the world, if you like. – But why isn't the end of the world as good as the beginning?'

'I suppose it isn't,' said Ursula, rather angry.

'Oh yes, ultimately,' he said. 'It means a new cycle of creation after – but not for us. If it is the end, then we are of the end – fleurs du mal if you like. If we are fleurs du mal, we are not roses of happiness, and there you are.'

'But I think I am,' said Ursula. 'I think I am a rose of happiness.'

'Ready-made?' he asked ironically.

'No – real,' she said, hurt.

'If we are the end, we are not the beginning,' he said.

'Yes, we are,' she said. 'The beginning comes out of the end.'

'After it, not out of it. After us, not out of us.'

'You are a devil, you know, really,' she said. 'You want to destroy our hope. You want us to be deathly.'

'No,' he said, 'I only want us to *know* what we are.'

'Ha!' she cried in anger. 'You only want us to know death.'

'You're quite right,' said the soft voice of Gerald, out of the dusk behind.

Birkin rose. Gerald and Gudrun came up. They all began to smoke, in the moments of silence. One after another, Birkin lighted their cigarettes. The match flickered in the twilight, and they were all smoking peacefully by the water-side. The lake was dim, the light dying from off it, in the midst of the dark land. The air all round was intangible, neither here nor there, and there was an unreal noise of banjoes, or suchlike music.

As the golden swim of light overhead died out, the moon gained brightness, and seemed to begin to smile forth her ascendancy. The dark woods on the opposite shore melted into universal shadow. And amid this universal under-shadow, there was a scattered intrusion of lights. Far down the lake were fantastic pale strings of colour, like beads of wan fire, green and red and yellow. The music came out in a little puff, as the launch, all illuminated, veered into the great shadow, stirring her outlines of half-living lights, puffing out her music in little drifts.

All were lighting up. Here and there, close against the faint water, and at the far end of the lake, where the water lay milky in the last whiteness of the sky, and there was no shadow, solitary, frail flames of lanterns floated from unseen boats. There was a sound of oars, and a boat passed from the pallor into the darkness under the wood, where her lanterns seemed to kindle into fire, hanging in ruddy lovely globes. And again, in the lake, shadowy red gleams hovered in reflection about the boat. Everywhere were these noiseless ruddy creatures of fire drifting near the surface of the water, caught at by the rarest, scarce visible reflections.

Birkin brought the lanterns from the bigger boat, and the four shadowy white figures gathered round, to light them.

Ursula held up the first, Birkin lowered the light from the rosy, glowing cup of his hands, into the depths of the lantern. It was kindled, and they all stood back to look at the great blue moon of light that hung from Ursula's hand, casting a strange gleam on her face. It flickered, and Birkin went bending over the well of light. His face shone out like an apparition, so unconscious, and again, something demoniacal. Ursula was dim and veiled, looming over him.

'That is all right,' said his voice softly.

She held up the lantern. It had a flight of storks streaming through a turquoise sky of light, over a dark earth.

'This is beautiful,' she said.

'Lovely,' echoed Gudrun, who wanted to hold one also, and lift it up full of beauty.

'Light one for me,' she said. Gerald stood by her, incapacitated. Birkin lit the lantern she held up. Her heart beat with anxiety, to see how beautiful it would be. It was primrose yellow, with tall straight flowers growing darkly from their dark leaves, lifting their heads into the primrose day, while butterflies hovered about them, in the pure clear light.

Gudrun gave a little cry of excitement, as if pierced with delight.

'Isn't it beautiful, oh, isn't it beautiful!'

Her soul was really pierced with beauty, she was translated beyond herself. Gerald leaned near to her, into her zone of light, as if to see. He came close to her, and stood touching her, looking with her at the primrose-shining globe. And she turned her face to his, that was faintly bright in the light of the lantern, and they stood together in one luminous union, close together and ringed with light, all the rest excluded.

Birkin looked away, and went to light Ursula's second lantern. It had a pale ruddy sea-bottom, with black crabs and seaweed moving sinuously under a transparent sea, that passed into flamy ruddiness above.

'You've got the heavens above, and the waters under the earth,' said Birkin to her.

'Anything but the earth itself,' she laughed, watching his live hands that hovered to attend to the light.

I'm dying to see what my second one is,' cried Gudrun, in a vibrating, rather strident voice, that seemed to repel the others from her.

Birkin went and kindled it. It was a lovely deep blue colour, with a red floor, and a great white cuttle-fish flowing in white soft streams all over it. The cuttle fish had a face that stared straight from the heart of the light, very fixed and coldly intent.

'How truly terrifying!' exclaimed Gudrun, in a voice of horror. Gerald, at her side, gave a low laugh.

'But isn't it really fearful?' she cried in dismay.

Again he laughed, and said:

'Change it with Ursula for the crabs.'

Gudrun was silent for a moment.

'Ursula,' she said, 'could you bear to have this fearful thing?'

'I think the colouring is *lovely*,' said Ursula.

'So do I,' said Gudrun. 'But could you *bear* to have it swinging to your boat? Don't you want to destroy it *at once*?'

'Oh no,' said Ursula. 'I don't want to destroy it.'

'Well, do you mind having it instead of the crabs? Are you sure you don't mind?'

Gudrun came forward to exchange lanterns.

'No,' said Ursula, yielding up the crabs and receiving the cuttlefish.

Yet she could not help feeling rather resentful at the way in which Gudrun and Gerald should assume a right over her, a precedence.

'Come then,' said Birkin. 'I'll put them on the boats.'

Moonlight on the lake, Roundhay Park, by Atkinson Grimshaw

He and Ursula were moving away to the big boat.

'I suppose you'll row me back, Rupert,' said Gerald, out of the pale shadow of the evening.

'Won't you go with Gudrun in the canoe?' said Birkin. 'It'll be more interesting.'

There was a moment's pause. Birkin and Ursula stood dimly, with their swinging lanterns, by the water's edge. The world was all illusive.

'Is that all right?' said Gudrun to him.

'It'll suit *me* very well,' he said. 'But what about you, and the rowing? I don't see why you should pull me.'

'Why not?' she said. 'I can pull you as well as I could pull Ursula.'

By her tone he could tell she wanted to have him in the boat to herself, and that she was subtly gratified that she should have power over them both. He gave himself, in a strange, electric submission.

She handed him the lanterns, whilst she went to fix the cane at the end of the canoe. He followed after her, and stood with the lanterns dangling against his white-flannelled thighs, emphasising the shadow around.

'Kiss me before we go,' came his voice softly from out of the shadow above.

She stopped her work in real, momentary astonishment.

'But why?' she exclaimed in pure surprise.

'Why?' he echoed, ironically.

And she looked at him fixedly for some moments. Then she leaned forward and kissed him, with a slow, luxurious kiss, lingering on the mouth. And then she took the lanterns from him, while he stood swooning with the perfect fire that burned in all his joints.

They lifted the canoe into the water, Gudrun took her place, and Gerald pushed off.

'Are you sure you don't hurt your hand, doing that?' she asked solicitous. 'Because I could have done it *perfectly*.'

'I don't hurt myself,' he said in a low, soft voice, that caressed her with inexpressible beauty.

And she watched him as he sat near her, very near to her, in the stern of the canoe, his legs coming towards hers, his feet touching hers. And she paddled softly, lingeringly, longing for him to say something meaningful to her. But he remained silent.

'You like this, do you?' she said, in a gentle, solicitous voice.

He laughted shortly.

'There is a space between us,' he said, in the same low, unconscious

124

voice, as if something were speaking out of him. And she was as if magically aware of their being balanced in separation in the boat. She swooned with acute comprehension and pleasure.

'But I'm very near,' she said caressively, gaily.

'Yet distant, distant,' he said.

Again she was silent with pleasure, before she answered, speaking with a reedy, thrilled voice:

'Yet we cannot very well change, whilst we are on the water.' – She caressed him subtly and strangely, having him completely at her mercy.

A dozen or more boats on the lake swung their rosy and moon-like lanterns low on the water, that reflected as from a fire. In the distance, the steamer twanged and thrummed and washed with her faintly splashing paddles, trailing her strings of coloured lights, and occasionally lighting up the whole scene luridly with an effusion of fireworks, Roman candles and sheafs of stars and other simple effects, illuminating the surface of the water, and showing the boats creeping round, low down. Then the lovely darkness fell again, the lanterns and the little threaded lights glimmered softly, there was a muffled knocking of oars and a waving of music.

Gudrun paddled almost imperceptibly. Gerald could see, not far ahead, the rich blue and the rose globes of Ursula's lanterns swaying softly cheek to cheek as Birkin rowed, and iridescent, evanescent gleams chasing in the wake. He was aware, too, of his own delicately coloured lights casting their softness behind him.

Gudrun rested her paddle and looked round. The canoe lifted with the lightest ebbing of the water. Gerald's white knees were very near to her.

'Isn't it beautiful!' she said softly, as if reverently.

She looked at him, as he leaned back against the faint crystal of the lantern-light. She could see his face, although it was a pure shadow. But it was a piece of twilight. And her breast was keen with passion for him, he was so beautiful in his male stillness and mystery. It was a certain pure effluence of maleness, like an aroma from his softly moulded contours, a certain rich perfection of his presence, that touched her with an ecstasy, a thrill of pure intoxication. She loved to look at him. For the present she did not want to touch him, to know the further, satisfying substance of his living body. He was purely intangible, yet so near. Her hands lay on the paddle like slumber, she only wanted to see him, like a crystal shadow, to feel his essential presence.

'Yes,' he said vaguely. 'It is very beautiful.'

He was listening to the faint near sounds, the dropping of water-drops from the oar-blades, the slight drumming of the lanterns behind him, as they rubbed against one another, the occasional rustling of Gudrun's full skirt, an alien land noise. His mind was almost submerged, he was almost transfused, lapsed out for the first time in his life, into the things about him. For he always kept such a keen attentiveness, concentrated and unyielding in himself. Now he had let go, imperceptibly he was melting into oneness with the whole. It was like pure, perfect sleep, his first great sleep of life. He had been so insistent, so guarded, all his life. But here was sleep, and peace, and perfect lapsing out.

'Shall I row to the landing-stage?' asked Gudrun wistfully.

'Anywhere,' he answered. 'Let it drift.'

'Tell me then, if we are running into anything,' she replied, in that very quiet, toneless voice of sheer intimacy.

'The lights will show,' he said.

So they drifted almost motionless, in silence.

Frieda Lawrence

Snake

In his essay 'The Reality of Peace', Lawrence had written:

> If there is a serpent of secret and shameful desire in my soul, let me not beat it out of my consciousness with sticks. It will lie beyond, in the marsh of the so-called subconsciousness, where I cannot follow it with sticks.

'Snake', written at Taormina, Sicily, in 1920, is one of the most finely achieved of the poems in Lawrence's splendid collection Birds, Beasts and Flowers. This volume represents the best of Lawrence at this period. He had given up on mankind –

> it is a world of Canaille; absolutely. Canaille, canaglia, Schweinhunderei, stinkpots. Pfui! – pish, pshaw, prrr! They all stink in my nostrils .... A curse, a murrain, a pox on this crawling, sniffling, spunkless brood of humanity

but nature could still move him to an appreciation of beauty. In a letter of 1916 he wrote:

> I saw a most beautiful brindled adder, in the spring, coiled up asleep with her head on her shoulder. She did not hear me till I was very near. Then she must have felt my motion, for she lifted her head like a queen to look, then turned and moved slowly and with delicate pride into the bushes. She often comes into my mind again, and I think I see her asleep in the sun, like a Princess of the fairy world. It is queer, the intimations of other worlds, which one catches.

A Snake, by Eric Gill

Snake

A snake came to my water-trough
On a hot, hot day, and I in pyjamas for the heat,
To drink there.

In the deep, strange-scented shade of the great dark carob-tree
I came down the steps with my pitcher
And must wait, must stand and wait, for there he was at the trough
    before me

He reached down from a fissure in the earth-wall in the gloom
And trailed his yellow-brown slackness soft-bellied down,
    over the edge of the stone trough
And rested his throat upon the stone bottom,
And where the water had dripped from the tap, in a small clearness,
He sipped with his straight mouth,
Softly drank through his staight gums, into his slack long body,
Silently.

Someone was before me at my water-trough,
And I, like a second-comer, waiting.

He lifted his head from his drinking, as cattle do,
And looked at me vaguely, as drinking cattle do,
And flickered his two-forked tongue from his lips, and mused a moment,
And stooped and drank a little more,
Being earth-brown, earth-golden from the burning bowels of the earth
On the day of Sicilian July, with Etna smoking.

The voice of my education said to me
He must be killed,
For in Sicily the black, black snakes are innocent, the gold are venomous.

And voices in me said, If you were a man
You would take a stick and break him now, and finish him off.

128

But must I confess how I liked him,
How glad I was he had come like a guest in quiet, to drink
    at my water-trough
And depart peaceful, pacified and thankless,
Into the burning bowels of this earth?

Was it cowardice, that I dared not kill him?
Was it perversity, that I longed to talk to him?
Was it humility, to feel so honoured?
I felt so honoured.

And yet those voices:
If you were not afraid, you would kill him!

And truly I was afraid, I was most afraid,
But even so, honoured still more
That he should seek my hospitality
From out the dark door of the secret earth.

He drank enough
And lifted his head, dreamily, as one who has drunken,
And flickered his tongue like a forked night on the air, so black,
Seeming to lick his lips,
And looked around like a god, unseeing, into the air,
And slowly turned his head,
And slowly, very slowly, as if thrice adream,
Proceeded to draw his slow length curving round
And climb again the broken bank of my wall-face.

And as he put his head into that dreadful hole,
And as he slowly drew up, snake-easing his shoulders, and
    entered farther,
A sort of horror, a sort of protest against his withdrawing into that
    horrid black hole,
Deliberately going into the blackness, and slowly drawing himself after,
Overcame me now his back was turned.

I looked round, I put down my pitcher,
I picked up a clumsy log
And threw it at the water-trough with a clatter.

Behind the Villa Mirenda, by D. H. Lawrence

I think it did not hit him,
But suddenly that part of him that was left behind convulsed
    in undignified haste,
Writhed like lightning, and was gone
Into the black hole, the earth-lipped fissure in the wall-front,
At which, in the intense still noon, I stared with fascination.

And immediately I regretted it.
I thought how paltry, how vulgar, what a mean act!
I despised myself and the voices of my accursed human education.

And I thought of the albatross,
And I wished he would come back, my snake.

For he seemed to me again like a king,
Like a king in exile, uncrowned in the underworld,
Now due to be crowned again.

And so, I missed my chance with one of the lords
Of life.
And I have something to expiate:
A pettiness.

The Elephant is Slow to Mate

'The Elephant is Slow to Mate' is one of the more successful of the little poems which Lawrence published in 1929 as Pansies because they were 'a bunch of pensées... a handful of thoughts': in his correspondence, Lawrence referred to them as 'rag poems'. Many of them are trivial and slipshod, or aimlessly amusing: others show true wit and genuine flashes of perception. Few of them have the reticence which makes this poem so moving.

An Indian Elephant, by Rembrandt

The Elephant is Slow to Mate

The elephant, the huge old beast,
   is slow to mate;
he finds a female, they show no haste
   they wait

for the sympathy in their vast shy hearts
   slowly, slowly to rouse
as they loiter along the river-beds
   and drink and browse

and dash in a panic through the brake
   of forest with the herd,
and sleep in massive silence, and wake
   together, without a word.

Slowly the great hot elephant hearts
   grow full of desire,
and the great beasts mate in secret at last,
   hiding their fire.

Oldest they are and the wisest of beasts
   so they know at last
how to wait for the loneliest of feasts
   for the full repast.

They do not snatch, they do not tear;
   their massive blood
moves as the moon-tides, near, more near
   till they touch in flood.

Tenderness

Lady Chatterley's Lover, *Lawrence's last novel, was always destined to be controversial. He wrote to his agents in 1927:*

> I am in quandary about my novel, *Lady Chatterley's Lover.* It's what the world would call very improper. But you know it's not really improper – I always labour at the same thing, to make the sex relation valid and precious, instead of shameful. And this novel is the furthest I've gone. To me it is beautiful and tender and frail as the naked self is.

Rather than risk a repetition of the suppression of The Rainbow, *Lawrence published the book himself in Italy, supplying it to subscribers in Britain and America. Nevertheless there was a furore. An anonymous writer in* John Bull *in 1928 confirmed Lawrence's worst fears about the book's reception, describing it, under the headline 'Famous Novelist's Shameful Book', as 'the most evil outpouring that has ever besmirched the literature of our country'. It was not until Penguin Books published the complete version in 1960 and defended it in the English courts that* Lady Chatterley *was generally available. Lawrence wrote the book three times, and the first two versions have also been published, as* The First Lady Chatterley *and* John Thomas and Lady Jane. *Both of these have their own charms, and indeed are in some ways better than the final text which contains, especially in its depiction of upper-class talk and manners, many absurdities. But at least in* Lady Chatterley *Lawrence progressed from the leadership fantasies of his mid-period fiction. He wrote to Witter Bynner in March 1928:*

> On the whole I agree with you, the leader–cum–follower relationship is a bore. And the new relationship will be some sort of tenderness.

Tenderness *was one of his suggested titles for his 'evil outpouring'. Another important aspect of the new novel was its English setting, strengthened by a final visit to Nottinghamshire in 1926. He wrote to Rolf Gardiner:*

> I was at my sister's in September, and we drove round – I saw the miners – and pickets – and policemen – it was like a spear through one's heart.

Lady Chatterley's Lover has little of the strident, hectoring tone which mars the leadership novels, and for all its clumsiness, contains many delicate and touching scenes. Few readers will forget, for instance, Connie's first, visionary glimpse of Mellors washing in the yard, 'quick, subtle as a weasel playing with water, and utterly alone'.

CONNIE WAS a good deal alone now, fewer people came to Wragby. Clifford no longer wanted them. He had turned against even the cronies. He was queer. He preferred the radio, which he had installed at some expense, with a good deal of success at last. He could sometimes get Madrid or Frankfurt, even there in the uneasy Midlands.

And he would sit alone for hours listening to the loudspeaker bellowing forth. It amazed and stunned Connie. But there he would sit, with a blank entranced expression on his face, like a person losing his mind, and listen, or seem to listen, to the unspeakable thing.

Was he really listening? Or was it some sort of soporific he took, whilst

Timber Team Stopping to Chat, by Edwin Frederick Holt

something else worked on underneath him? Connie did not know. She fled up to her room, or out of doors to the wood. A kind of terror filled her sometimes, a terror of the incipient insanity of the whole civilized species.

But now that Clifford was drifting off to this other weirdness of industrial activity, becoming almost a *creature*, with a hard, efficient shell of an exterior and a pulpy interior, one of the amazing crabs and lobsters of the modern, industrial and financial world, invertebrates of the crustacean order, with shells of steel, like machines, and inner bodies of soft pulp, Connie herself was really completely stranded.

She was not even free, for Clifford must have her there. He seemed to have a nervous terror that she should leave him. The curious pulpy part of him, the emotional and humanly-individual part, depended on her with terror, like a child, almost an idiot. She must be there, there at Wragby, a Lady Chatterley, his wife. Otherwise he would be lost like an idiot on a moor.

This amazing dependence Connie realized with a sort of horror. She heard him with his pit managers, with the members of his Board, with young scientists, and she was amazed at his shrewd insight into things, his power, his uncanny material power over what is called practical men. He had become a practical man himself, and an amazingly astute and powerful one, a master. Connie attributed it to Mrs Bolton's influence upon him, just at the crisis in his life.

But this astute and practical man was almost an idiot when left alone to his own emotional life. He worshipped Connie. She was his wife, a higher being, and he worshipped her with a queer, craven idolatory, like a savage, a worship based on enormous fear, and even hate of the power of the idol, the dread idol. All he wanted was for Connie to swear, to swear not to leave him, not to give him away.

'Clifford,' she said to him – but this was after she had the key to the hut – 'Would you really like me to have a child one day?'

He looked at her with a furtive apprehension in his rather prominent pale eyes.

'I shouldn't mind, if it made no difference between us,' he said.

'No difference to what?' she asked.

'To you and me; to our love for one another. If it's going to affect that, then I'm all against it. Why, I might even one day have a child of my own!'

She looked at him in amazement.

'I mean, it might come back to me one of these days.'

She still stared in amazement, and he was uncomfortable.

'So you would not like it if I had a child?' she said.

'I tell you,' he replied quickly, like a cornered dog, 'I am quite willing, provided it doesn't touch your love for me. If it would touch that, I am dead against it.'

Connie could only be silent in cold fear and contempt. Such talk was really the gabbling of an idiot. He no longer knew what he was talking about.

'Oh, it wouldn't make any difference to my feeling for you,' she said, with a certain sarcasm.

'There!' he said. 'That is the point! In that case I don't mind in the least. I mean it would be awfully nice to have a child running about the house, and feel one was building up a future for it. I should have something to strive for then, and I should know it was your child, shouldn't I, dear? And it would seem just the same as my own. Because it is you who count in these matters. You know that, don't you, dear? I don't enter, I am a cypher. You are the great I-am! as far as life goes. You know that, don't you? I mean, as far as I am concerned. I mean, but for you I am absolutely nothing. I live for your sake and your future. I am nothing to myself.'

Connie heard it all with deepening dismay and repulsion. It was one of the ghastly half-truths that poison human existence. What man in his senses would say such things to a woman! But men aren't in their senses. What man with a spark of honour would put this ghastly burden of life-responsibility upon a woman, and leave her there, in the void?

Moreover, in half an hour's time, Connie heard Clifford talking to Mrs Bolton, in a hot, impulsive voice, revealing himself in a sort of passion-less passion to the woman, as if she were half mistress, half foster-mother to him. And Mrs Bolton was carefully dressing him in evening clothes, for there were important business guests in the house.

Connie really sometimes felt she would die at this time. She felt she was being crushed to death by weird lies, and by the amazing cruelty of idiocy. Clifford's strange business efficiency in a way over-awed her, and his declaration of private worship put her into a panic. There was nothing between them. She never even touched him nowadays, and he never touched her. He never even took her hand and held it kindly. No, and because they were so utterly out of touch, he tortured her with his declaration of idolatry. It was the cruelty of utter impotence. And she felt her reason would give way, or she would die.

She fled as much as possible to the wood. One afternoon, as she sat brooding, watching the water bubbling coldly in John's Well, the keeper had strode up to her.

'I got you a key made, my Lady!' he said, saluting, and he offered her the key.

'Thank you so much!' she said, startled.

'The hut's not very tidy, if you don't mind,' he said. 'I cleared it what I could.'

'But I didn't want you to trouble!' she said.

'Oh, it wasn't any trouble. I am setting the hens in about a week. But they won't be scared of you. I s'll have to see to them morning and night, but I shan't bother you any more than I can help.'

'But you wouldn't bother me,' she pleaded. 'I'd rather not go to the hut at all, if I am going to be in the way.'

He looked at her with his keen blue eyes. He seemed kindly, but distant. But at least he was sane, and wholesome, if even he looked thin and ill. A cough troubled him.

'You have a cough,' she said.

'Nothing – a cold! The last pneumonia left me with a cough, but it's nothing.'

He kept his distance from her, and would not come any nearer.

She went fairly often to the hut, in the morning or in the afternoon, but he was never there. No doubt he avoided her on purpose. He wanted to keep his own privacy.

He had made the hut tidy, put the little table and chair near the fireplace, left a little pile of kindling and small logs, and put the tools and traps away as far as possible, effacing himself. Outside, by the clearing, he had built a low little roof of boughs and straw, a shelter for the birds, and under it stood the five coops. And, one day when she came, she found two brown hens sitting alert and fierce in the coops, sitting on pheasant's eggs, and fluffed out so proud and deep in all the heat of the pondering female blood. This almost broke Connie's heart. She, herself, so forlorn and unused, not a female at all, just a mere thing of terrors.

Then all the five coops were occupied by hens, three brown and a grey and a black. All alike, they clustered themselves down on the eggs in the soft nestling ponderosity of the female urge, the female nature, fluffing our their feathers. And with brilliant eyes they watched Connie, as she crouched before them, and they gave short sharp clucks of anger and alarm, but chiefly of female anger at being approached.

Bluebells, by Daniel Sherrin

Connie found corn in the corn-bin in the hut. She offered it to the hens in her hand. They would not eat it. Only one hen pecked at her hand with a fierce little jab, so Connie was frightened. But she was pining to give them something, the brooding mothers who neither fed themselves nor drank. She brought water in a little tin, and was delighted when one of the hens drank.

Now she came every day to the hens, they were the only things in the world that warmed her heart. Clifford's protestations made her go cold from head to foot. Mrs Bolton's voice made her go cold, and the sound of the business men who came. An occasional letter from Michaelis affected her with the same sense of chill. She felt she would surely die if it lasted much longer.

Yet it was spring, and the bluebells were coming in the wood, and the leaf-buds on the hazels were opening like the spatter of green rain. How terrible that it should be spring, and everything cold-hearted, cold-hearted. Only the hens, fluffed so wonderfully on the eggs, were warm with their hot, brooding female bodies! Connie felt herself living on the brink of fainting all the time.

Then, one day, a lovely sunny day with great tufts of primroses under the hazels, and many violets dotting the paths, she came in the afternoon to the coops and there was one tiny, tiny perky chicken tinily prancing round in front of a coop, and the mother hen clucking in terror. The slim little chick was greyish brown with dark markings, and it was the most alive little spark of a creature in seven kingdoms at that moment. Connie crouched to watch in a sort of ecstasy. Life, life! Pure, sparky, fearless new life! New life! So tiny and so utterly without fear! Even when it scampered a little, scrambling into the coop again, and disappeared under the hen's feathers in answer to the mother hen's wild alarm-cries, it was not really frightened, it took it as a game, the game of living. For in a moment a tiny sharp head was poking through the gold-brown feathers of the hen, and eyeing the Cosmos.

Connie was fascinated. And at the same time, never had she felt so acutely the agony of her own female forlornness. It was becoming unbearable.

She had only one desire now, to go to the clearing in the wood. The rest was a kind of painful dream. But sometimes she was kept all day at Wragby, by her duties as hostess. And she felt as if she too were going blank, just blank and insane.

One evening, guests or no guests, she escaped after tea. It was late, and she fled across the park like one who fears to be called back. The sun was setting rosy as she entered the wood, but she pressed on among the flowers. The light would last long overhead.

She arrived at the clearing flushed and semi-conscious. The keeper was there, in his shirt-sleeves, just closing up the coops for the night, so the little occupants would be safe. But still one little trio was pattering about on tiny feet, alert drab mites, under the straw shelter, refusing to be called in by the anxious mother.

'I had to come and see the chickens!' she said, panting, glancing shyly at the keeper, almost unaware of him. 'Are there any more?'

'Thirty-six so far!' he said. 'Not bad!'

He too took a curious pleasure in watching the young things come out.

Connie crouched in front of the last coop. The three chicks had run in. But still their cheeky heads came poking sharply through the yellow feathers, then withdrawing, then only one beady little head eyeing forth from the vast mother-body.

'I'd love to touch them,' she said, putting her fingers gingerly through the bars of the coop. But the mother-hen pecked at her hand fiercely, and Connie drew back startled and frightened.

'How she pecks at me! She hates me!' she said in a wondering voice. 'But I wouldn't hurt them.'

The man standing above her laughed, and crouched down beside her, knees apart, and put his hand with quiet confidence slowly into the coop. The old hen pecked at him, but not so savagely. And slowly, softly, with sure gentle fingers, he felt among the old bird's feathers and drew out a faintly-peeping chick in his closed hand.

'There!' he said, holding out his hand to her. She took the drab little thing between her hands, and there it stood, on its impossible little stalks of legs, its atom of balancing life trembling through its almost weightless feet into Connie's hands. But it lifted its handsome, clean-shaped little head boldly, and looked sharply round, and gave a little 'peep'. 'So adorable! So cheeky!' she said softly.

The keeper, squatting beside her, was also watching with an amused face the bold little bird in her hands. Suddenly he saw a tear fall on to her wrist.

And he stood up, and stood away, moving to the other coop. For suddenly he was aware of the old flame shooting and leaping up in his loins, that he had hoped was quiescent for ever. He fought against it, turning his back to her. But it leapt, and leapt downwards, circling in his

141

knees.

He turned again to look at her. She was kneeling and holding her two hands slowly forward, blindly, so that the chicken should run in to the mother-hen again. And there was something so mute and forlorn in her, compassion flamed in his bowels for her.

Without knowing, he came quickly towards her and crouching beside her again, taking the chick from her hands, because she was afraid of the hen, and putting it back in the coop. At the back of his loins the fire suddenly darted stronger.

He glanced apprehensively at her. Her face was averted, and she was crying blindly, in all the anguish of her generation's forlornness. His heart melted suddenly, like a drop of fire, and he put out his hand and laid his fingers on her knee.

'You shouldn't cry,' he said softly.

But then she had her hands over her face and felt that really her heart was broken and nothing mattered any more.

He laid his hand on her shoulder, and softly, gently, it began to travel down the curve of her back, blindly, with a blind stroking motion, to the curve of her crouched loins. And there his hand softly, softly, stroked the curve of her flank, in the blind instinctive caress.

She had found her scrap of handkerchief and was blindly trying to dry her face.

'Shall you come to the hut?' he said, in a quiet, neutral voice.

And closing his hand softly over her upper arm, he drew her up and led her slowly to the hut, not letting go of her till she was inside. Then he cleared aside the chair and table, and took a brown, soldier's blanket from the tool chest, spreading it slowly. She glanced at his face, as she stood motionless.

His face was pale and without expression, like that of a man submitting to fate.

'You lie there,' he said softly, and he shut the door, so that it was dark, quite dark.

With a queer obedience, she lay down on the blanket. Then she felt the soft, groping, helplessly desirous hand touching her body, feeling for her face. The hand stroked her face softly, with infinite soothing and assurance, and at last there was the soft touch of a kiss on her cheek.

She lay quite still, in a sort of sleep, in a sort of dream. Then she quivered as she felt his hand groping softly, yet with a queer thwarted clumsiness, among her clothing. Yet the hand knew, too, how to

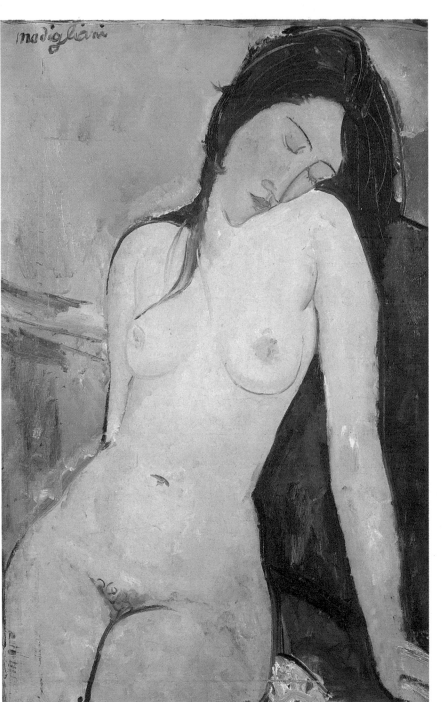

Seated Nude, by Amedeo Modigliani

143

unclothe her where it wanted. He drew down the thin silk sheath, slowly, carefully, right down and over her feet. Then with a quiver of exquisite pleasure he touched the warm soft body, and touched her navel for a moment in a kiss. And he had to come in to her at once, to enter the peace on earth of her soft, quiescent body. It was the moment of pure peace for him, the entry into the body of the woman.

She lay still, in a kind of sleep, always in a kind of sleep. The activity, the orgasm was his, all his; she could strive for herself no more. Even the tightness of his arms round her, even the intense movement of his body, and the springing of his seed in her, was a kind of sleep, from which she did not begin to rouse till he had finished and lay softly panting against her breast.

Then she wondered, just dimly wondered, why? Why was this necessary? Why had it lifted a great cloud from her and given her peace? Was it real? Was it real?

Her tormented modern-woman's brain still had no rest. Was it real? And she knew, if she gave herself to the man, it was real. But if she kept herself for herself, it was nothing. She was old; millions of years old, she felt. And at last, she could bear the burden of herself no more. She was to be had for the taking. To be had for the taking.

The man lay in a mysterious stillness. What was he feeling? What was he thinking? She did not know. He was a strange man to her, she did not know him. She must only wait, for she did not dare to break his mysterious stillness. He lay there with his arms round her, his body on hers, his wet body touching hers, so close. And completely unknown. Yet not unpeaceful. His very stillness was peaceful.

She knew that, when at last he roused and drew away from her. It was like an abandonment. He drew her dress in the darkness down over her knees and stood for a few moments, apparently adjusting his own clothing. Then he quietly opened the door and went out.

She saw a very brilliant little moon shining above the afterglow over the oaks. Quickly she got up and arranged herself; she was tidy. Then she went to the door of the hut.

All the lower wood was in shadow, almost darkness. Yet the sky overhead was crystal. But it shed hardly any light. He came through the lower shadow towards her, his face lifted like a pale blotch.

'Shall we go then?' he said.

'Where?'

'I'll go with you to the gate.'

The Triumph, by Blair Hughes-Stanton

He arranged things his own way. He locked the door of the hut and came after her.

'You aren't sorry, are you?' he asked, as he went at her side.

'No! No! Are you? she said.

'For that! No!' he said. Then after a while he added: 'But there's the rest of things.'

'What rest of things?' she said.

'Sir Clifford. Other folks. All the complications.'

'Why complications?' she said, disappointed.

'It's always so. For you as well as for me. There's always complications.' He walked on steadily in the dark.

'And are you sorry?' she said.

'In a way!' he replied, looking up at the sky. 'I thought I'd done with it all. Now I've begun again.'

'Begun what?'

Life.'

What Ails Thee?

Another 'Pansy', this comic dialogue shows Lawrence able to poke fun at himself. Clearly he was not unaware of the ludicrous side of Mellors and Lady Chatterley's conversations, though he took Lady Chatterley's Lover *utterly seriously. All Lawrence's friends remembered him as a gay and amusing companion, full of jokes and laughter; a far cry from the tortured prophet of the popular imagination.*

What Ails Thee?

What ails thee then, woman, what ails thee?
doesn't ter know?

If tha canna say't, come then an' scraight it out on my bosom!
Eh? – Men doesna ha'e bosoms? 'appen not, on'y tha knows
    what I mean.
Come then, tha can scraight it out on my shirt-front an' tha'lt feel better.

  – In the first place, I don't scraight.
  And if I did, I certainly couldn't *scraight it out*.
  And if I could, the last place I should choose
  would be your shirt-front
  or your manly bossom either.
  So leave off trying to put the Robbie Burns touch over me
  and kindly hand me the cigarettes
  if you haven't smoked them all,
  which you're much more likely to do
  than to shelter anybody from the cau-auld blast.

Portrait of a lady, by Augustus John

The Flying Fish

The three chapters below are all that Lawrence wrote of a proposed novel, The Flying Fish. They were dictated to Frieda following Lawrence's near-fatal attack of malaria in 1925, during which the extent of his tuberculosis was first diagnosed. He told his friends Earl and Achsah Brewster, 'I've an intuition I shall not finish that novel. It was written so near the borderline of death, that I never have been able to carry it through, in the cold light of day.' So it remained a fragment, but a fragment almost perfect in its incompletion. The passage in chapter 2 describing the school of dolphins is one of the most beautiful in rhythm and feeling in all of Lawrence's prose; he was thinking, perhaps, of the dolphins painted in the Tomb of the Lionesses in Tarquinia, which he described in Etruscan Places: 'all around the room, the dolphins are leaping, leaping all downwards into the rippling sea'. He told the Brewsters how the story would end: 'The last part will be regenerate man, a real life in this Garden of Eden.'

1 Departure from Mexico

'COME HOME else no Day in Daybrook.' This cablegram was the first thing Gethin Day read of the pile of mail which he found at the hotel in the lost town of South Mexico, when he returned from his trip to the coast. Though the message was not signed, he knew whom it came from and what it meant.

He lay in his bed in the hot October evening, still sick with malaria. In the flush of fever he saw yet the parched, stark mountains of the south, the villages of reed huts lurking among the trees, the black-eyed natives with the lethargy, the ennui, the pathos, the beauty of an exhausted race; and above all he saw the weird, uncanny flowers, which he had hunted down from the high plateaux, through the valleys, and down to the steaming crocodile heat of the *tierra caliente*, towards the sandy, burning, intolerable shores. For he was fascinated by the mysterious green blood that runs in the veins of plants, and the purple and yellow and red blood that colours the faces of the flowers. Especially the unknown flora of South Mexico attracted him, and above all he wanted to trace to the living plant the mysterious essences and toxins known with such strange elaboration to the Mayas, the Zapotecas, and the Aztecs.

His head was humming like a mosquito, his legs were paralysed for the

Pueblo Indian Dancers, by D.H. Lawrence

moment by the heavy quinine injection the doctor had injected into them, and his soul was as good as dead with the malaria; so he threw all his letters unopened on the floor, hoping never to see them again. He lay with the pale yellow cablegram in his hand: 'Come home else no Day in Daybrook.' Through the open doors from the patio of the hotel came the heavy scent of that invisible green night-flower the natives call *Buena de Noche*. The little Mexican servant-girl strode in barefoot with a cup of tea, her flounced cotton skirt swinging, her long black hair down her back. She asked him in her birdlike Spanish if he wanted nothing more. '*Nada más*,' he said. 'Nothing more; leave me and shut the door.'

He wanted to shut out the scent of that powerful green inconspicuous night-flower he knew so well.

No Day in Daybrook;
For the Vale a bad outlook.

149

D.H. Lawrence with his sister, Emily

No Day in Daybrook! There had been Days in Daybrook since time began: at least, so he imagined.

Daybrook was a sixteenth-century stone house, among the hills in the middle of England. It stood where Crichdale bends to the south and where Ashleydale joins in. 'Daybrook standeth at the junction of the ways and at the centre of the trefoil. Even it rides within the Vale as an ark between three seas; being indeed the ark of these vales, if not of all England.' So had written Sir Gilbert Day, he who built the present Daybrook in the sixteenth century. Sir Gilbert's *Book of Days*, so beautifully written out on vellum and illuminated by his own hand, was one of the treasures of the family.

Sir Gilbert had sailed the Spanish seas in his day, and had come home rich enough to rebuild the old house of Daybrook according to his own fancy. He had made it a beautiful pointed house, rather small, standing upon a knoll above the river Ashe, where the valley narrowed and the woods rose steep behind. 'Nay,' wrote this quaint Elizabethan, 'though I say that Daybrook is the ark of the Vale, I mean not the house itself, but He that Day, that lives in the house in his day. While Day there be in

Daybrook, the floods shall not cover the Vale nor shall they ride over England completely.'

Gethin Day was nearing forty, and he had not spent much of his time in Daybrook. He had been a soldier and had wandered in many countries. At home his sister Lydia, twenty years older than himself, had been the Day in Daybrook. Now from her cablegram he knew she was either ill or already dead.

She had been rather hard and grey like the rock of Crichdale, but faithful and a pillar of strength. She had let him go his own way, but always when he came home, she would look into his blue eyes with her searching uncanny grey eyes and ask: 'Well, have you come, or are you still wandering?' 'Still wandering, I think,' he said. 'Mind you don't wander into a cage one of these days,' she replied; 'you would find far more room for yourself in Daybrook than in these foreign parts, if you knew how to come into your own.'

This had always been the burden of her song to him: *if you knew how to come into your own.* And it had always exasperated him with a sense of futility; though whether his own futility or Lydia's, he had never made out.

Lydia was wrapt up in old Sir Gilbert's *Book of Days*; she had written out for her brother a fair copy, neatly bound in green leather, and had given it him without a word when he came of age, merely looking at him with that uncanny look of her grey eyes, expecting something of him, which always made him start away from her.

The *Book of Days* was a sort of secret family bible at Daybrook. It was never shown to strangers, nor ever mentioned outside the immediate family. Indeed in the family it was never openly alluded to. Only on solemn occasions, or on rare evenings, at twilight when the evening star shone, had the father, now dead, occasionally read aloud to the two children from the nameless work.

In the copy she had written for Gethin, Lydia had used different coloured inks in different places. Gethin imagined that her favourite passages were those in the royal-blue ink, where the page was almost as blue as the cornflowers that grew tall beside the walks in the garden at Daybrook.

'Beauteous is the day of the yellow sun which is the common day of men; but even as the winds roll unceasing above the trees of the world, so doth that Greater Day, which is the Uncommon Day, roll over the unclipt bushes of our little daytime. Even also as the morning sun shakes his yellow wings on the horizon and rises up, so the great bird beyond him spreads out his dark blue feathers, and beats his wings in the tremor of the Greater Day.'

Gethin knew a great deal of his *Book of Days* by heart. In a dilettante fashion, he had always rather liked highflown poetry, but in the last years, something in the hard, fierce, finite sun of Mexico, in the dry terrible land, and in the black staring eyes of the suspicious natives, had made the ordinary day lose its reality to him. It had cracked like some great bubble, and to his uneasiness and terror, he had seemed to see through the fissures the deeper blue of that other Greater Day where moved the other sun shaking its dark blue wings. Perhaps it was the

D.H. Lawrence in Oaxaca

malaria; perhaps it was his own inevitable development; perhaps it was the presence of those handsome, dangerous, wide-eyed men left over from the ages before the flood in Mexico, which caused his old connections and his accustomed world to break for him. He was ill, and he felt as if at the very middle of him, beneath his navel, some membrane were torn, some membrane which had connected him with the world and its day. The natives who attended him, quiet, soft, heavy, and rather helpless, seemed, he realized, to be gazing from their wide black eyes always into that greater day whence they had come and where they wished to return. Men of a dying race, to whom the busy sphere of the common day is a cracked and leaking shell.

He wanted to go home. He didn't care now whether England was tight and little and over-crowded and far too full of furniture. He no longer minded the curious quiet atmosphere of Daybrook in which he felt he would stifle as a young man. He no longer resented the weight of family tradition, nor the peculiar sense of authority which the house seemed to have over him. Now he was sick from the soul outwards, and the common day had cracked for him, and the uncommon day was showing him its immensity, he felt that home was the place. It did not matter that England was small and tight and over-furnished, if the Greater Day were round about. He wanted to go home, away from these big wild countries where men were dying back into the Greater Day, home where he dare face the sun behind the sun, and come into his own in the Greater Day.

But he was as yet too ill to go. He lay in the nausea of the tropics, and let the days pass over him. The door of his room stood open on to the patio where green banana trees and high strange-sapped flowering shrubs rose from the water-sprinkled earth towards that strange rage of blue which was the sky over the shadow-heavy, perfume-soggy air of the closed-in courtyard. Dark-blue shadows moved from the side of the patio, disappeared, then appeared on the other side. Evening had come, and the barefoot natives in white calico flitted with silent rapidity across, and across, for ever going, yet mysteriously going nowhere, threading the timelessness with their transit, like swallows of darkness.

The window of the room, opposite the door, opened on to the tropical parched street. It was a big window, came nearly down to the floor, and was heavily barred with upright and horizontal bars. Past the window went the natives, with the soft, light rustle of their sandals. Big straw hats balanced, dark cheeks, calico shoulders brushed with the silent swiftness of the Indian past the barred window-space. Sometimes children clutched the bars and gazed in, with great shining eyes and straight blue-black hair, to see the Americano lying in the majesty of a white bed. Sometimes a beggar stood there, sticking a skinny hand through the iron grille and whimpering the strange, endless, pullulating whimper of the beggar – *'por amore de Dios!'* – on and on and on, as it seemed for an eternity. But the sick man on the bed endured it with the same endless endurance in resistance, endurance in resistence which he had learned in the Indian countries. Aztec or Mixtec, Zapotec or Maya, always the same power of serpent-like torpor of resistance.

The doctor came – an educated Indian: though he could do nothing but inject quinine and give a dose of calomel. But he was lost between two days, the fatal greater day of the Indians, the fussy, busy lesser day of the white people.

'How is it going to finish?' he said to the sick man, seeking a word. 'How is it going to finish with the Indians, with the Mexicans? Now the soldiers are all taking *marihuana* – hashish!'

'They are all going to die. They are all going to kill themselves – all – all,' said the Englishman, in the faint permanent delirium of his malaria. 'After all, beautiful it is to be dead, and quite departed.'

The doctor looked at him in silence, understanding only too well. 'Beautiful it is to be dead!' It is the refrain which hums at the centre of every Indian heart, where the greater day is hemmed in by the lesser. The despair that comes when the lesser day hems in the greater. Yet the doctor looked at the gaunt white man in malice: – 'What, would you have us quite gone, you Americans?'

At last, Gethin crawled out into the plaza. The square was like a great low fountain of green and of dark shade, now it was autumn and the rains were over. Scarlet craters rose the canna flowers, licking great red tongues, and tropical yellow. Scarlet, yellow, green, blue-green, sunshine intense and invisible, deep indigo shade! and small, white-clad natives pass, passing, across the square, through the green lawns, under the indigo shade, and across the hollow sunshine of the road into the arched arcades of the low Spanish buildings, where the shops were. The low, baroque Spanish buildings stood back with a heavy, sick look, as if they too felt the endless malaria in their bowels, the greater day of the stony Indian crushing the more jaunty, lean European day which they represented. The yellow cathedral leaned its squat, earthquake-shaken towers, the bells sounded hollow. Earth-coloured tiny soldiers lay and stood around the entrance to the municipal palace, which was so baroque and Spanish, but which now belonged to the natives. Heavy as a strange bell of shadow-coloured glass, the shadow of the greater day hung over this coloured plaza which the Europeans had created, like an oasis, in the lost depths of Mexico. Gethin Day sat half lying on one of the broken benches, while tropical birds flew and twittered in the great trees, and natives twittered or flitted in silence, and he knew that here, the European day was annulled again. His body was sick with the poison that lurks in all tropical air, his soul was sick with that other day, that rather awful greater day which permeates the little days of the old races. He wanted to get out, to get out of this ghastly tropical void into which he had fallen.

Yet it was the end of November before he could go. Little revolutions had again broken the thread of railway at the end of which the southern town hung revolving like a spider. It was a narrow-gauge railway, one single narrow little track which ran over the plateau, then slipped down, down the long *barranca*, descending five thousand feet down to the valley which was a cleft in the plateau, then up again seven thousand feet, to the higher plateau to the north. How easy to break the thread! One of the innumerable little wooden bridges destroyed, and it was done. The three hundred miles to the north was impassable wilderness, like the hundred and fifty miles through the low-lying jungle to the south.

At last however he could crawl away. The train came again. He had cabled to England, and had received the answer that his sister was dead. It seemed so natural, there under the powerful November sun of southern Mexico, in the drugging, powerful odours of the night-flowers, that Lydia should be dead. She seemed so much more real, shall we say actually vital, in death. Dead, he could think of her as quite near and comforting and real, whereas while she was alive, she was so utterly alien, remote and fussy, ghost-like in her petty Derbyshire day.

'For the little day is like a house with the family round the hearth, and the door shut. Yet outside whispers the Greater Day, wall-less, and hearthless. And the time will come at last when the walls of the little day shall fall, and what is left of the family of men shall find themselves outdoors in the Greater Day, houseless and abroad, even here between the knees of the Vales, even in Crichdale. It is a doom that will come upon tall men. And then they will breathe deep, and be breathless in the great air, and salt sweat will stand on their brow, thick as buds on sloe-bushes when the sun comes back. And little men will shudder and die out, like clouds of grasshoppers falling in the sea. Then tall men will remain alone in the land, moving deeper in the Greater Day, and moving deeper. Even as the flying fish, when he leaves the air and recovereth his element in the depth, plunges and invisibly rejoices. So will tall men rejoice, after their flight of fear, through the thin air, pursued by death. For it is on wings of fear, sped from the mouth of death, that the flying fish riseth twinkling in the air, and rustles in astonishment silvery through the thin small day. But he dives again into the great peace of the deeper day, and under the belly of death, and passes into his own.'

Gethin read again his *Book of Days*, in the twilight of his last evening. Personally, he resented the symbolism and mysticism of his Elizabethan ancestor. But it was in his veins. And he was going home, back, back to the house with the flying fish on the roof. He felt an immense doom over everything, still the same the next morning, when, an hour after dawn, the little train ran out from the doomed little town, on to the plateau, where the cactus thrust up its fluted tubes, and where mountains stood back, blue, cornflower-blue, so dark and pure in form, in the land of the Greater Day, the day of demons. The little train, with two coaches, one full of natives, the other with four or five 'white' Mexicans, ran fussily on, in the little day of toys and men's machines. On the roof sat tiny, earthy-looking soldiers, faces burnt black, with cartridge-belts and rifles. They clung on tight, not to be shaken off. And away went this weird toy, this crazy little caravan, over the great lost land of cacti and mountains standing back, on to the shut-in defile where the long descent began.

At half past ten, at a station some distance down the *barranca*, a station connected with old silver mines, the train stood, and all descended to eat: the eternal turkey and black sauce, potatoes, salad, and apple pie – the American apple pie, which is a sandwich of cooked apple between two layers of pie-crust. And also beer, from Puebla. Two Chinamen administered the dinner, in all the decency, cleanness and well-cookedness of the little day of the white men, which they reproduce so well. There it was, the little day of our civilization. Outside, the little train waited. The little black-faced soldiers sharpened their knives. The vast varying declivity of the *barranca* stood in sun and shadow as on the day of doom, untouched.

On again, winding, descending the huge and savage gully or crack in the plateau-edge, where no men lived. Bushes trailed with elegant pink creeper, such as is seen in hothouses, enormous blue convolvuluses opened out, and in the unseemly tangle of growth, bulbous orchids jutted out from trees, and let hang a trail of white or yellow flower. The strange, entangled squalor of the jungle.

Gethin Day looked down the ravine, where water was running. He saw four small deer lifting their heads from drinking, to look at the train. '*Los venados! los venados!*' he heard the soldiers softly calling. As if knowing they were safe, the deer stood and wondered, away there in the Greater Day, in the manless space, while the train curled round a sharp jutting rock.

They came at last to the bottom, where it was very hot, and a few wild men hung round with the sword-like knives of the sugar-cane. The train seemed to tremble with fear all the time, as if its thread might be cut. So frail, so thin the thread of the lesser day, threading with its business the great reckless heat of the savage land. So frail a thread, so easily snapped!

Mexico, by José Maria Velasco

But the train crept on, northwards, upwards. And as the stupor of heat began to pass, in the later afternoon, the sick man saw among mango trees, beyond the bright green stretches of sugar-cane, white clusters of a village, with the coloured dome of a church all yellow and blue with shiny majolica tiles. Spain putting the bubbles of her little day among the blackish trees of the unconquerable.

He came at nightfall to a small square town, more in touch with civilization, where the train ended its frightened run. He slept there. And next day he took another scrap of a train across to the edge of the main plateau. The country was wild, but more populous. An occasional big *hacienda* with sugar-mills stood back among the hills. But it was silent. Spain had spent the energy of her little day here, now the silence, the terror of the Greater Day, mysterious with death, was filling in again.

On the train a native, a big, handsome man, wandered back and forth among the uneasy Mexican travellers with a tray of glasses of ice-cream. He was no doubt of the Tlascala tribe. Gethin Day looked at him and met his glistening dark eyes. '*Quiere helados, Señor?*' said the Indian, reaching a glass with his dark, subtle-skinned, workless hand. And in the soft, secret tones of his voice, Gethin Day heard the sound of the Greater Day. '*Gracias!*'

'*Padrón! Padrón!*' moaned a woman at the station. '*Por amor de Dios, Padrón!*' and she held out her hand for a few centavos. And in the moaning croon of her Indian voice the Englishman heard again the fathomless crooning appeal of the Indian women, moaning stranger, more terrible than the ring-dove, with a sadness that had no horizon, and a rocking, moaning appeal that drew out the very marrow of the soul of a man. Over the door of her womb was written not only: '*Lasciate ogni speranza voi ch'entrate,*' but: '*Perdite ogni pianto, voi ch'uscite.*' For the men who had known these women were beyond weeping and beyond even despair, mute in the timeless compulsion of the Greater Day. Big, proud men could sell glasses of ice-cream at twenty-five centavos, and not really know they were doing it. They were elsewhere, beyond despair. Only sometimes the last passion of death-lust would sweep them, shut up as they were in the white man's lesser day, belonging as they did to the greater day.

The little train ran on to the main plateau, and to the junction with the main-line railway, called the Queen's Own, a railway that still belongs to the English, and that joins Mexico city with the Gulf of Mexico. Here, in the big but forlorn railway restaurant the Englishman ordered the regular meal, that came with American mechanical take-it-or-leave-it flatness. He ate what he could, and went out again. There the vast plains were level and bare, under the blue winter sky, so pure, and not too hot, and in the distance the white cone of the volcano of Orizaba stood perfect in the middle air.

'There is no help, O man. Fear gives thee wings like a bird, death comes after thee open-mouthed, and thou soarest on the wind like a fly. But thy flight is not far, and thy flying is not long. Thou art a fish of the timeless Ocean, and must needs fall back. Take heed lest thou break thyself in the fall! For death is not in dying, but in the fear. Cease then the struggle of thy flight, and fall back into the deep element where death is and is not, and life is not a fleeing away. It is beauteous thing to live and to be alive. Live then in the Greater Day, and let the waters carry thee, and the flood bear thee long, and live, only live, no more of this hurrying away.'

'No more of this hurrying away.' Even the Elizabethans had known it, the restlessness, the 'hurrying away'. Gethin Day knew he had been hurrying away. He had hurried perhaps a little too far, just over the edge. Now, try as he might, he was aware of a gap in his time-space continuum; he was, in the words of his ancestor, aware of the Greater Day showing through the cracks in the ordinary day. And it was useless trying to fill up the cracks. The little day was destined to crumble away, as far as he was concerned, and he would *have* to inhabit the greater day. The very sight of the volcano cone in mid-air made him know it. His little self was used up, worn out. He felt sick and frail, facing this change of life.

'Be still, then, be still! Wrap thyself in patience, shroud thyself in peace, as the tall volcano clothes himself in snow. Yet he looks down in him, and sees wet sun in him molten and of great force, stirring with the scald sperm of life. Be still, above the sperm of life, which spills alone in its hour. Be still, as an apple on its core, as a nightingale in winter, as a long-waiting mountain upon its fire. Be still, upon thine own sun.'

'For thou hast a sun in thee. Thou hast a sun in thee, and it is not timed. Therefore wait. Wait, and be at peace with thine own sun, which is thy sperm of life. Be at peace with thy sun in thee, as the volcano is, and the dark holly-bush before berry-time, and the long hours of night. Abide by thy sun in thee, even the onion doth so, though you see it not. Yet peel her, and her sun in thine eyes maketh tears. Each thing hath its little sun, even in the wicked house-fly something twinkleth.'

Standing there on the platform of the station open to the great plains of the plateau, Gethin Day said to himself: My old ancestor is more real to me than the restaurant, and the dinner I have eaten, after all. The train still did not come. He turned to another page of cornflower-blue writing, hoping to find something amusing.

'When earth inert lieth too heavy, then Vesuvius spitteth out fire. And if a nightingale would not sing, his song unsung in him would slay him. For to the nightingale his song is Nemesis, and unsung songs are the Erinyes, the impure Furies of vengeance. And thy sun in thee is thy all in all, so be patient, and take no care. Take no care, for what thou knowest is ever less than what thou art. The full fire even of thine own sun in thine own body, thou canst never know. So how shouldst thou load care upon thy sun? Take heed, take thought, take pleasure, take pain, take all things as thy sun stirs. Only fasten not thyself in care about anything, for care is impiety, it spits upon the sun.'

It was the white and still volcano, visionary across the swept plain, that looked back at him as he glanced up from his *Book of Days*. But there the train came, thundering, with all the mock majesty of great equipage, and the Englishman entered the Pullman car, and sat with his book in his pocket.

The train, almost with the splendour of the Greater Day, yet rickety and foolish at last, raced on the level, entered the defile, and crept, cautiously twining round and round, down the cliff-face of the plateau, with the low lands lying thousands of feet below, specked with a village or two like fine specks. Yet the low lands drew up, and the pine trees were gone far above, and at last the thick trees crowded the line, and dark-faced natives ran beside the train selling gardenias, gardenia perfume heavy in all the air. But the train was nearly empty.

Veracruz at night-fall was a modern stone port, but disheartened and tropical, mostly shut up, abandoned, as if life had quietly left it. Great customs buildings, unworking, acres of pianofortes in packing-cases, all the endless jetsam of the little day of commerce flung up here and waiting, acres of goods unattended to, waiting till the labour of Veracruz should cease to be on strike. A town, a port struck numb, the inner sun striking vengefully at the little life of commerce. The day's sun set, there was a heavy orange light over the water, something sinister, a gloom, a deep resentment in nature, even in the washing of the warm sea. In these salt waters natives were still baptized to Christianity, and the socialists, in mockery perhaps, baptized themselves into the mystery of frustration and revenge. The port was in the hands of strikers and wild out-of-workers, and was blank. Officials had almost disappeared. Even here, a woman, a 'lady' examined the passports.

But the ship rode at the end of the jetty: the one lonely passenger ship. There was one other steamer – from Sweden, a cargo boat. For the rest, the port was deserted. It was a point where the wild primeval day of this continent met the busy white man's day, and the two annulled one another. The result was a port of nullity, nihilism concrete and actual, calling itself the city of the True Cross.

2 The Gulf

In the morning they sailed off, away from the hot shores, from the high land hanging up inwards. And world gives place to world. In an hour, it was only ship and ocean, the world of land and affairs was gone.

There were few people on board. In the second-class saloon only seventeen souls. Gethin Day was travelling second. It was a German boat, he knew it would be clean and comfortable. The second class fare was already forty-five pounds. And a man who is not rich, and who would live his life under as little compulsion as possible, must calculate keenly with money and its power. For the lesser day of money and the mealy-mouthed Mammon is always ready for a victim, and a man who has glimpsed the Greater Day, and the inward sun, will not fall into the clutches of Mammon's mean day, if he can help it. Gethin Day had a moderate income, and he looked on this as his bulwark against Mammon's despicable authority. The thought of earning a living was repulsive and humiliating to him.

In the first-class saloon were only four persons: two Danish merchants, stout and wealthy, who had been part of a bunch of Danish business men invited by the Mexican government to look at the business resources of the land. They had been fêted and feasted, and shown what they were meant to see, so now, fuller of business than ever, they were going back to Copenhagen to hatch the eggs they had conceived. But they had also eaten oysters in Veracruz, and the oysters also were inside them. They fell sick of poison, and lay deathly ill all the voyage, leaving only the other first-class passengers, an English knight and his son, alone in their glory. Gethin Day was sincerely glad he had escaped the first class, for the voyage was twenty days.

The seventeen souls of the second class were four of them English, two Danish, five Spaniards, five Germans and a Cuban. They all sat at one long table in the dining-saloon, the Cuban at one end of the table, flanked by four English on his left, facing the five Spaniards across the table. Then came the two Danes, facing one another, and being buffer-state between the rest and the five Germans, who occupied the far end of the table. It was a German boat, so the Germans were very noisy, and the stewards served them first. The Spaniards and the Cuban were mum, the English were stiff, the Danes were uneasy, the Germans were boisterous, and so the first luncheon passed. It was the lesser day of the ship, and small enough. The menu being in correct German and doubtful Spanish, the Englishwoman on Gethin Day's right put up a lorgnette and stared at it. She was unable to stare it out of countenance, so she put it down and ate uninformed as to what she was eating. The Spaniard opposite Gethin Day had come to table without a collar or tie, doing the bluff, go-to-hell colonial touch, almost in his shirt-sleeves. He was a man of about thirty-two. He brayed at the steward in strange, harsh Galician Spanish, the steward grinned somewhat sneeringly and answered in German, having failed to understand, and not prepared to exert himself to try. Down the table a blonde horse of a woman was shouting at the top of her voice, in harsh North-German, to a Herr Doktor with turned-up moustaches who presided at the German head of the table. The Spaniards bent forward in a row to look with a sort of silent horror at the yelling woman, then they looked at one another with a faint grimace of mocking repulsion. The Galician banged the table with the empty wine decanter: wine was 'included'. The steward, with a sneering little grin at such table-manners, brought a decanter half full. Wine was not *ad lib*, but *à discrétion*. The Spaniards, having realized this, henceforth snatched it quickly and pretty well emptied the decanter before the English got a shot at it. Which somewhat amused the table stewards, who wanted to see the two foreign lots fight it out. But Gethin Day solved this problem by holding out his hand to the fat, clean-shaven Basque, as soon as the decanter reached that gentleman, and saying: 'May I serve the lady?' Whereupon the Basque handed over the decanter, and Gethin helped the two ladies and himself, before handing back the decanter to the Spaniards. – Man wants but little here below, but he's damn well got to see he gets it. – All this is part of the little day, which has to be seen to. Whether it is interesting or not depends on one's state of soul.

Bristling with all the bristles of offence and defence which a man has to put up with the first days in such company, Gethin Day would go off down the narrow gangway of the bottom deck, down into the steerage, where the few passengers lay about in shirt and trousers, on to the very front tip of the boat.

She was a long, narrow, old ship, long like a cigar, and not much space in her. Yet she was pleasant, and had a certain grace of her own, was a real ship, not merely a 'liner'. She seemed to travel swift and clean, piercing away into the Gulf.

Gethin Day would sit for hours at the very tip of the ship, on the

The Steamship 'Philadelphia', by Antonio Jacobsen

bowsprit, looking out into the whitish sunshine of the hot Gulf of Mexico. Here he was alone, and the world was all strange white sunshine, candid, and water, warm, bright water, perfectly pure beneath him, of an exquisite frail green. It lifted vivid wings from the running tip of the ship, and threw white pinion-spray from its green edges. And always, always, always it was in the two-winged fountain, as the ship came like life between, and always the spray fell swishing, pattering from the green arch of the water-wings. And below, as yet untouched, a moment ahead, always a moment ahead, and perfectly untouched, was the lovely green depth of the water, depth, deep, shallow-pale emerald above an under sapphire-green, dark and pale, blue and shimmer-green, two waters, many waters, one water, perfect in unison, one moment ahead of the ship's bows, so serene, fathomless and pure and free of time. It was very lovely, and on the softly-lifting bowsprit of the long, swift ship the body was cradled in the sway of timeless life, the soul lay in the jewel-coloured moment, the jewel-pure eternity of this gulf of nowhere.

And always, always, like a dream, the flocks of flying fish swept into the air, from nowhere, and went brilliantly twinkling in their flight of silvery watery wings rapidly fluttering, away, low as swallows over the smooth curved surface of the sea, then gone again, vanished, without splash or evidence, gone. One alone like a little silver twinkle. Gone! The sea was still and silky-surfaced, blue and softly heaving, empty, purity itself, sea, sea, sea.

Then suddenly the faint whispering crackle, and a cloud of silver on webs of pure, fluttering water was soaring low over the surface of the sea, at an angle from the ship, as if jetted away from the cut-water, soaring in a low arc, fluttering with the wild emphasis of grasshoppers or locusts suddenly burst out of the grass, in a wild rush to make away, make away, and making it, away, away, then suddenly gone, like a lot of lights blown out in one breath. And still the ship did not pause, any more than the moon pauses, neither to look nor catch breath. But the soul pauses and holds its breath, for wonder, wonder, which is the very breath of the soul.

All the long morning he would be there curled in the wonder of this gulf of creation, where the flying fishes on translucent wings swept in their ecstatic clouds out of the water, in a terror that was brilliant as joy, in a joy brilliant with terror, with wings made of pure water flapping with great speed, and long-shafted bodies of translucent silver like squirts of living water, there in air, brilliant in air, before suddenly they had disappeared, and the blue sea was trembling with a delicate frail surface of green, the still sea lay one moment ahead, untouched, untouched since time began, in its watery loveliness. .

Sometimes a ship's officer would come and peer over the edge and look at him lying there. But nothing was said. People didn't like looking over the edge. It was too beautiful, too pure and lovely, the Greater Day. They shoved their snouts a moment over the rail, then withdrew, faintly abashed, faintly sneering, faintly humiliated. After all, they showed snouts, nothing but snouts, to the unbegotten morning, so they might well be humiliated.

Sometimes an island, two islands, three, would show up, dismal and small, with the peculiar American gloom. No land! The soul wanted to see land. Only the uninterrupted water was purely lovely, pristine.

And the third morning there was a school of porpoises leading the ship. They stayed below surface all the time, so there was no hullabaloo of human staring. Only Gethin Day saw them. And what joy! what joy of life! what marvellous pure joy of being a porpoise within the great sea, of being many porpoises heading and mocking in translucent onrush the menacing, yet futile onrush of a vast ship!

It was a spectacle of the purest and most perfected joy in life that Gethin

Dolphins from an Etruscan tomb

Day ever saw. The porpoises were ten or a dozen, round-bodied torpedo fish, and they stayed there as if they were not moving, always there, with no motion apparent, under the purely pellucid water, yet speeding on at just the speed of the ship, without the faintest show of movement, yet speeding on in the most miraculous precision of speed. It seemed as if the tail-flukes of the last fish exactly touched the ship's bows, under-water, with the frailest, yet precise and permanent touch. It seemed as if nothing moved, yet fish and ship swept on through the tropical ocean. And the fish moved, they changed places all the time. They moved in a little cloud, and with the most wonderful sport they were above, they were below, they were to the fore, yet all the time the same one speed, the same one speed, and the last fish just touching with his tail-flukes, the iron cut-water of the ship. Some would be down in the blue, shadowy, but horizontally motionless in the same speed. Then with a strange revolution, these would be up in pale green water, and others would be down. Even the toucher, who touched the ship, would in a twinkling be changed. And ever, ever the same pure horizontal speed, sometimes a dark back skimming the water's surface light, from beneath, but never the surface broken. And ever the last fish touching the ship, and ever the others speeding in motionless, effortless speed, and intertwining with strange silkiness as they sped, intertwining among one another, fading down to the dark blue shadow, and strangely emerging again among the silent, swift others, in pale green water. All the time, so swift, they seemed to be laughing.

Gethin Day watched spell-bound, minute after minute, an hour, two hours, and still it was the same, the ship speeding, cutting the water, and the strong-bodied fish heading in perfect balance of speed underneath, mingling among themselves in some strange single laughter of multiple consciousness, giving off the joy of life, sheer joy of life, togetherness in pure complete motion, many lusty-bodied fish enjoying one laugh of life, sheer togetherness, perfect as passion. They gave off into the water their marvellous joy of life, such as the man had never met before. And it left him wonderstruck.

'But they know joy, they know pure joy!' he said to himself in amazement. 'This is the most laughing joy I have ever seen, pure and unmixed. I always thought flowers had brought themselves to the most beautiful perfection in nature. But these fish, these fleshy, warm-bodied fish achieve more than flowers, heading along. This is the purest achievement of joy I have seen in all life: these strong, careless fish. Men have not got in them that secret to be alive together and make one like a single laugh, yet each fish going his own gait. This is sheer joy – and men have lost it, or never accomplished it. The cleverest sportsmen in the world are owls beside these fish. And the togetherness of love is nothing to the spinning unison of dolphins playing under-sea. It would be wonderful to know joy as these fish know it. The life of the deep waters is ahead of us, it contains sheer togetherness and sheer joy. We have never got there.'

There as he leaned over the bowsprit he was mesmerized by one thing only, by joy, by joy of life, fish speeding in water with playful joy. No wonder Ocean was still mysterious, when such red hearts beat in it! No wonder man, with his tragedy, was a pale and sickly thing in comparison! What civilization will bring us to such a pitch of swift laughing togetherness, as these fish have reached?

3 The Atlantic

The ship came in the night to Cuba, to Havana. When she became still, Gethin Day looked out of his port-hole and saw little lights on upreared darkness. Havana!

They went on shore next morning, through the narrow dock-streets near the wharf, to the great boulevard. It was a lovely warm morning, already early December, and the town was in the streets, going to mass, or coming out of the big, unpleasant old churches. The Englishman wandered with the two Danes for an hour or so, in the not very exciting city. Many Americans were wandering around, and nearly all wore badges of some sort. The city seemed, on the surface at least, very American. And underneath, it did not seem to have any very deep character of its own left.

The three men hired a car to drive out and about. The elder of the Danes, a man of about forty-five, spoke fluent colloquial Spanish, learned on the oil-fields of Tampico. 'Tell me,' he said to the chauffeur, 'why do all these *americanos*, these Yankees, wear badges on themselves?'

He spoke, as foreigners nearly always do speak of the Yankees, in a tone of half-spiteful jeering.

'Ah, Señor,' said the driver, with a Cuban grin. 'You know they all come here to drink. They drink so much that they all get lost at night, so they all wear a badge: name, name of hotel, place where it is. Then our policemen find them in the night, turn them over as they lie on the pavement, read name, name of hotel, and place, and so they are put on a cart and carted home. Ah, the season is only just beginning. Wait a week or two, and they will lie in the streets at night like a battle, and the police doing Red Cross work, carting them to their hotels. Ah, *los americanos*! They are so good. You know they own us now. Yes, they own us. They own Havana. We are a Republic owned by the Americans. *Muy bien*, we give them drink, they give us money. Bah!'

And he grinned with a kind of acrid indifference. He sneered at the whole show, but he wasn't going to do anything about it.

The car drove out to the famous beer-gardens, where all drank beer – then to the inevitable cemetery, which almost rivalled that of New Orleans. 'Every person buried in this cemetery guarantees to put up a tomb-monument costing not less than fifty-thousand dollars.' Then they drove past the new suburb of villas, springing up neat and tidy, spick-and-span, same all the world over. Then they drove out into the country, past the old sugar *haciendas* and to the hills.

And to Gethin Day it was all merely depressing and void of real interest. The Yankees owned it all. It had not much character of its own. And what character it had was the peculiar, dreary character of all America wherever it is a little abandoned. The peculiar gloom of Connecticut or New Jersey, Louisiana or Georgia, a sort of dreariness in the very bones of the land, that shows through immediately the human effort sinks. How quickly the gloom and the inner dreariness of Cuba must have affected the spirit of the Conquistadores, even Columbus!

They drove back to the town and ate a really good meal, and watched a stout American couple, apparently man and wife, lunching with a bottle of champagne, a bottle of hock, and a bottle of Burgundy for the two of them, and apparently drinking them all at once. It made one's head reel.

The bright, sunny afternoon they spent on the esplanade by the sea. There the great hotels were still shut. But they had, so to speak, half an eye open: a tea-room going, for example.

And Day thought again, how tedious the little day can be! How difficult to spend even one Sunday looking at a city like Havana, even if one has spent the morning driving into the country. The infinite tedium of looking at things! the infinite boredom of things anyhow. Only the rippling, bright, pale-blue sea, and the old fort gave one a feeling of life. The rest, the great esplanade, the great boulevard, the great hotels, all seemed what they were, dead, dried concrete, concrete, dried deadness.

Everybody was thankful to be back on the ship for dinner, in the dark loneliness of the wharves. See Naples and die. Go seeing any place and you'll be half dead of exhaustion and tedium by dinner time.

So! goodbye Havana! The engines were going before breakfast time. It was a bright blue morning. Wharves and harbour slid past, the high bows moved backwards. Then the ship deliberately turned her back on Cuba and the sombre shore, and began to move north, through the blue day, which passed like a sleep. They were moving now into wide space.

The next morning they woke to greyness, grey low sky, and hideous low grey water, and a still air. Sandwiched between two greynesses, the long, wicked old ship sped on, as unto death.

'What's happened?' Day asked of one of the officers.

'We have come north, to get into the current running east. We come north about the latitude of New York, then we run due east with the stream.'

'What a wicked shame!'

And indeed it was. The sun was gone, the blueness was gone, life was gone. The Atlantic was like a cemetery, an endless, infinite cemetery of greyness, where the bright, lost world of Atlantis is buried. It was December, grey, dark December on a waste of ugly, dead-grey water, under a dead-grey sky.

And so they ran into a swell, a long swell whose oily, sickly waves seemed hundreds of miles long, and travelling in the same direction as the ship's course. The narrow cigar of a ship heaved up the up-slope with a nauseating heave, up, up, up, till she righted for a second sickeningly on the top, then tilted, and her screw raced like a dentist's burr in a hollow tooth. Then down she slid, down the long, shivering down-slope, leaving all her guts behind her, and the guts of all the passengers too. In an hour, everybody was deathly white, and sickily grinning, thinking it a sort of joke that would soon be over. Then everybody disappeared, and the game went on: up, up, up, heavingly up, till a pause, ah! – then burr-rr-rr! as the screw came out of the water and shattered every nerve. Then whoooosh! the long and awful downrush, leaving the entrails behind.

She was like a plague-ship, everybody disappeared, stewards and everybody. Gethin Day felt as if he had taken poison: and he slept – slept, slept, slept, and yet was all the time aware of the ghastly motion – up, up, up, heavingly up, then ah! one moment, followed by the shattering burr-rr-rr! and the unspeakable ghastliness of the downhill slither, where death seemed inside the entrails, and water chattered like the after-death. He was aware of the hour-long moaning, moaning of the Spanish doctor's fat, pale Mexican wife, two cabins away. It went on for ever. Everything went on for ever. Everything was like this for ever, for ever. And he slept, slept, slept, for thirty hours, yet knowing it all, registering just the endless repetition of the motion, the ship's loud squeaking and chirruping, and the ceaseless moaning of the woman.

Suddenly at tea-time the second day he felt better. He got up. The ship was empty. A ghastly steward gave him a ghastly cup of tea, then disappeared. He dozed again, but came to dinner.

There were three people at the long table, in the horribly travelling grey silence: himself, a young Dane, and the elderly, dried Englishwoman. She talked, talked. The three looked in terror at *Sauerkraut* and smoked loin of pork. But they ate a little. Then they looked out on the utterly repulsive, grey, oily, windless night. Then they went to bed again.

The third evening it began to rain, and the motion was subsiding. They were running out of the swell. But it was an experience to remember.

The North Country

First published in New Poems *in 1918, 'The North Country' represents Lawrence's mature view of industrialised man. In New York in 1922, Lawrence was asked what he would do to save the world. He replied with vehemence, 'I thought... you understood that I hoped it would go to pieces as rapidly and completely as possible.' The only hope was to wake out of numbness into a new life.*

The North Country

In another country, black poplars shake themselves over a pond,
And rooks and the rising smoke-waves scatter and wheel from
   the works beyond;
The air is dark with north and with sulphur, the grass is a darker green,
And people darkly invested with purple move palpable
   through the scene.

Soundlessly down across the counties, out of the resonant gloom
That wraps the north in stupor and purple travels the deep, slow boom
Of the man-life north-imprisoned, shut in the hum of the purpled steel
As it spins to sleep on its motion, drugged dense in the sleep of the wheel.

Out of the sleep, from the gloom of motion, soundlessly, somnambule
Moans and booms the soul of a people imprisoned, asleep in the rule
Of the strong machine that runs mesmeric, booming the spell of its word
Upon them and moving them helpless, mechanic, their will to
   its will deferred.

Sunset and Industry, by Charles Longbotham

Yet all the while comes the droning inaudible, out of the violet air,
The moaning of sleep-bound beings in travail that toil and are
  will-less there
In the spell-bound north, convulsive now with a dream near
  morning, strong
With violent achings heaving to burst the sleep that is now not long.

A Dream of Life

This odd fantasy is the second half of a late piece of writing published posthumously as an 'Autobiographical Fragment'. And that is what it is, to start with, a sober account of Eastwood (called here, 'Newthorpe') rather like Lawrence's essay on 'Nottingham and the Mining Countryside', emphasising 'the general effect of paltriness, smallness, meaness, fathomless ugliness, combined with a sort of chapel-going respectability.' But then, slowly, the writing changes texture, and a childhood memory turns into a Utopian dream. This dream is, perhaps, the 'real life in this Garden of Eden' which Gethin Day was to find at the end of The Flying Fish. *It was written just after* Etruscan Places, *and Lawrence's future citizens of Newthorpe are strongly reminiscent of his ancient Etruscans:*

> Their nakedness is its own clothing, more easy than drapery. The curves of their limbs show pure pleasure in life, a pleasure that goes deeper still in the limbs of the dancers, in the big, long hands thrown out and dancing to the very ends of the fingers, a dance that surges from within, like a current in the sea.

UP FROM Moorgreen goes a footpath past the quarry and up the fields, out to Renshaw's farm. This was always a favourite walk of mine. Beside the path lies the old quarry, part of it very old and deep and filled in with oak trees and guelder-rose and tangle of briars, the other part open, with square wall neatly built up with dry-stone on the side under the plough-fields, and the bed still fairly level and open. This open part of the quarry was blue with dog-violets in spring, and, on the smallish brambles, the first handsome blackberries came in autumn. Thank heaven, it is late October, and too late for blackberries, or there would still be here some wretched men with baskets, ignominiously combing the brambles for the last berry. When I was a boy, how a man, a full-grown miner, would have been despised for going with a little basket lousing the hedges for a blackberry or two. But the men of my generation put their pride in their

172

pocket, and now their pockets are empty.

The quarry was a haunt of mine, as a boy. I loved it because, in the open part, it seemed so sunny and dry and warm, the pale stone, the pale, slightly sandy bed, the dog-violets and the early daisies. And then the old part, the deep part, was such a fearsome place. It was always dark – you had to crawl under bushes. And you came upon honeysuckle and nightshade, that no one ever looked upon. And at the dark sides were little, awful rocky caves, in which I imagined the adders lived.

There was a legend that these little caves or niches in the rocks were 'everlasting wells', like the everlasting wells at Matlock. At Matlock the water drips in caves, and if you put an apple in there, or a bunch of grapes, or even if you cut your hand off and put it in, it won't decay, it will turn everlasting. Even if you put a bunch of violets in, they won't die, they'll turn everlasting.

Later, when I grew up and went to Matlock – only sixteen miles away – and saw the infamous everlasting wells, that the water only made a hoary nasty crust of stone on everything, and the stone hand was only a glove stuffed with sand, being 'petrified', I was disgusted. But still, when I see the stone fruits that people have in bowls for decoration, purple, semi-translucent stone grapes, and lemons, I think: *these* are the real fruits from the everlasting wells.

In the soft, still afternoon I found the quarry not very much changed. The red berries shone quietly on the briars. And in this still, warm, secret place of the earth I felt my old childish longing to pass through a gate, into a deeper, sunnier, more silent world.

The sun shone in, but the shadows were already deep. Yet I had to creep away into the darkness of the bushes, into the lower hollow of the tree-filled quarry. I felt, as I had always felt, there was something there. And as I wound my way, stooping, through the unpleasant tangle, I started, hearing a sudden rush and clatter of falling earth. Some part of the quarry must be giving way.

I found the place, away at the depth under the trees and bushes, a new place where yellow earth and whitish earth and pale rock had slid down new in a heap. And at the top of the heap was a crack, a little slantingly upright slit or orifice in the rock.

I looked at the new place curiously, the pallid new earth and the rock among the jungle of vegetation, the little opening above, into the earth. A touch of sunlight came through the oak-leaves and fell on the new place and the aperture, and the place flashed and twinkled. I had to climb up to look at it.

It was a little crystalline cavity in the rock, all crystal, a little pocket or womb of quartz, among the common stone. It was pale and colourless, the stuff we call spar, from which they make little bowls and mementoes, in Matlock. But through the flat-edged, colourless crystal of the spar ran a broad vein of purplish crystal, wavering inwards as if it were arterial. And that was a vein of the Blue John spar that is rather precious.

The place fascinated me, especially the vein of purple, and I had to clamber into the tiny cave, which would just hold me. It seemed warm in there, as if the shiny rock were warm and alive, and it seemed to me there was a strange perfume of rock, of living rock like hard, bright flesh, faintly perfumed with phlox. It was a subtle yet most fascinating secret perfume, an inward perfume. I crept right into the little cavity, into the narrow inner end where the vein of purple ran, and I curled up there, like an animal in its hole. 'Now,' I thought, 'for a little while I am safe and sound, and the vulgar world doesn't exist for me.' I curled together with soft, curious voluptuousness. The scent of inwardness and of life, a queer scent like phlox, with a faint narcotic inner quality like opium or like truffles, became very vivid to me, then faded. I suppose I must have gone to sleep.

Later, I don't know how much later, it may have been a minute, or an eternity, I was wakened by feeling something lifting me, lifting me with a queer, half-sickening motion, curiously exciting, in a slow little rhythmic heave that was at once soft and powerful, gentle and violent, grateful and violating. I could do nothing, not even wake up: yet I was not really terrified, only utterly wonderstruck.

Then the lifting and heaving ceased, and I was cold. Something harsh passed over me: I realized it was my face: I realized I had a face. Then immediately a sharpness and bitingness flew into me, flew right into me, through what must have been my nostrils, into my body, what must have been my breast. Roused by a terrific shock of amazement, suddenly a new thing rushed into me, right into me, with a sweep that swept me away, and at the same time I felt that first thing moving somewhere in me, there was a movement that came aloud.

There were some dizzy moments when my I, my consciousness, wheeled and swooped like an eagle that is going to wheel away into the sky and be gone. Yet I felt her, my I, my life, wheeling closer, closer, my consciousness. And suddenly she closed with me, and I knew, I came awake.

I knew. I knew I was alive. I even heard a voice say: 'He's alive!' Those were the first words I heard.

And I opened my eyes again and blinked with terror, knowing the light of day. I shut them again, and felt sensations out in space, somewhere, and yet upon *me*. Again my eyes were opened, and even saw objects, great things that were here and were there and then were not there. And the sensations out in space drew nearer, as it were, to me, the middle me.

So consciousness swooped and swerved, returning in great swoops. I realized that I was I, and that this I was also a body that ended abruptly in feet and hands. Feet! yes, feet! I remembered even the word. Feet!

I roused a little, and saw a greyish pale nearness that I recognized was my body, and something terrible moving upon it and making sensations in it. Why was it grey, my own nearness? Then I felt that other sensation, that I call aloudness, and I knew it. It was 'Dust of ages!' That was the aloudness: 'Dust of Ages!'

In another instant I knew that violent movingness that was making sensations away out upon me. It was somebody. In terror and wonder the realization came to me: it was somebody, another one, a man. A man, making sensations on me! A man, who made the aloudness: 'Dust of Ages.' A man! Still I could not grasp it. The conception would not return whole to me.

Yet once it had lodged within me, my consciousness established itself. I moved. I even moved my legs, my far-off feet. Yes! And an aloudness came out of me, even of me. I knew, I even knew now that I had a throat. And in another moment I should know something else.

It came to me all of a sudden. I saw the man's face. I saw it, a ruddy sort of face with a nose and a trimmed beard. I even knew more. I said: 'Why?'

And the face quickly looked at me, with blue eyes into my eyes, and I struggled as if to get up.

'Art awake?' it said.

And somewhere, I knew there was the word Yes! But it had not yet come to me.

But I knew, I knew! Dimly I came to know that I was lying in the sun on new earth that was spilled before my little, opened cave. I remembered my cave. But why should I be lying grey and stark-naked on earth in the sun outside I did not know; nor what the face was, nor whose.

Then there was more aloudness, and there was another one. I realized there could be more than one other one. More than one! More than one! I felt a new sudden something that made all of me move at once, in many directions, it seemed, and I became once more aware of the extent of me, and an aloudness came from my throat. And I remembered even that new something that was upon me. Many sensations galloping in all directions! But it was one dominant, drowning. It was water. Water! I even remembered water, or I knew I knew it. They were washing me. I even looked down and saw the whiteness: me, myself, white, a body.

And I remembered, that when all of me had moved to the touch of water, and I had made an aloudness in my throat, the men had laughed. Laughed! I remembered laughter.

So they washed me, I came to myself. I even sat up. And I saw earth and rock, and a sky that I knew was afternoon. And I was stark-naked, and there were two men washing me, and they too were stark-naked. But I was white, pure white, and thin, and they were ruddy, and not thin.

They lifted me, and I leaned on one, standing, while the other washed me. The one I leaned on was warm, and his life softly warmed me. The other one rubbed me gently. I was alive. I saw my white feet like two curious flowers, and I lifted them one after another, remembering walking.

The one held me, and the other put a woollen shirt or smock over me. It was pale grey and red. Then they fastened shoes on my feet. Then the free one went to the cave, peering, and he came back with things in his hands: buttons, some discoloured yet unwasted coins, a dull but not rusted pocket-knife, a waistcoat buckle, and a discoloured watch, whose face was very dark. Yet I knew these things were mine.

'Where are my clothes?' I said.

I felt eyes looking at me, two blue eyes, two brown eyes, full of strange life.

'My clothes!' I said.

They looked at one another, and made strange speech. Then the blue-eyed one said to me:

'Gone! Dust of ages!'

They were strange men to me, with their formal, peaceful faces and trimmed beards, like old Egyptians. The one on whom I was unconsciously leaning stood quite still, and he was warmer than the afternoon sunshine. He seemed to give off life to me, I felt a warmth suffusing into me, an inflooding of strength. My heart began to lift with strange, exultant strength. I turned to look at the man I was resting on, and met the blue, quiet shimmer of his eyes. He said something to me, in the quiet, full voice, and I nearly understood, because it was like the dialect.

The Sunderers, by Blair Hughes-Stanton

He said it again, softly and calmly, speaking to the inside of me, so that I
understood as a dog understands, from the voice, not from the words.

'Can ta goo, o shollt be carried?'

It sounded to me like that, like the dialect.

'I think I can walk,' said I, in a voice that sounded harsh after the soft,

177

deep modulation of the other.

He went slowly down the heap of loose earth and stones, which I remembered had fallen. But it was different. There were no trees in an old quarry hollow. This place was bare, like a new working. And when we came out, it was another place altogether. Below was a hollow of trees, and a bare, grassy hillside swept away, with clumps of trees, like park-land. There was no colliery, no railway, no hedges, no square, shut-in fields. And yet the land looked tended.

We stood on a little path of paved stone, only about a yard wide. Then the other man came up from the quarry, carrying tools and wearing a grey shirt or smock with a red cord. He spoke with that curious soft inwardness, and we turned down the path, myself still leaning on the shoulder of the first man. I felt myself quivering with a new strength, and yet ghostlike. I had a curious sensation of lightness, not touching the ground as I walked, as if my hand that rested on the man's shoulder buoyed me up. I wanted to know whether I was really buoyant, as in a dream.

I took my hand suddenly from the man's shoulder, and stood still. He turned and looked at me.

'I can walk alone,' I said, and as in a dream I took a few paces forward. It was true. I was filled with a curious rushing strength that made me almost buoyant, scarcely needing to touch the ground. I was curiously, quiveringly strong, and at the same time buoyant.

'I can go alone!' I said to the man.

They seemed to understand, and to smile, the blue-eyed one showing his teeth when he smiled. I had a sudden idea: How beautiful they are, like plants in flower! But still, it was something I felt, rather than saw.

The blue-eyed one went in front, and I walked on the narrow path with my rushing buoyancy, terribly elated and proud, forgetting everything, the other man following silently behind. Then I was aware that the path had turned and ran beside a road in a hollow where a stream was, and a cart was clanking slowly ahead, drawn by two oxen and led by a man who was entirely naked.

I stood still, on the raised, paved path, trying to think, trying, as it were, to come awake. I was aware that the sun was sinking behind me, golden in the October afternoon. I was aware that the man in front of me also had no clothes on whatsoever, and he would soon be cold.

Then I made an effort, and looked round. On the slopes to the left were big, rectangular patches of dark plough-land. And men were ploughing

178

still. On the right were hollow meadows, beyond the stream, with tufts of trees and many speckled cattle being slowly driven forwards. And in front the road swerved on, past a mill-pond, and a few little houses, and then swerved up a rather steep hill. And at the top of the hill was a town, all yellow in the late afternoon light, with yellow, curved walls rising massive from the yellow-leaved orchards, and above, buildings swerving in a long, oval curve, and round, faintly conical towers rearing up. It had something at once soft and majestical about it, with its soft yet powerful curves, and no sharp angles or edges, the whole substance seeming soft and golden like the golden flesh of a city.

And I knew, even while I looked at it, that it was the place where I was born, the ugly colliery townlet of dirty red brick. Even as a child, coming home from Moorgreen, I had looked up and seen the squares of miners' dwellings, built by the Company, rising from the hill-top in the afternoon light like the walls of Jerusalem, and I had wished it were a golden city, as in the hymns we sang in the Congregational Chapel.

Now it had come true. But the very realization, and the very intensity of my *looking*, had made me lose my strength and my buoyancy. I turned forlorn to the men who were with me. The blue-eyed one came and took my arm, and laid it across his shoulders, laying his left hand round my waist, on my hip.

And almost immediately the soft, warm rhythm of his life pervaded me again, and the memory in me which was my old self went to sleep. I was like a wound, and the touch of these men healed me at once. We went on again, along the raised pavement.

Three horsemen came cantering up, from behind. All the world was turning home towards the town, at sunset. The horsemen slackened pace as they came abreast. They were men in soft, yellow sleeveless tunics, with the same still, formal Egyptian faces and trimmed beards as my companions. Their arms and legs were bare and they rode without stirrups. But they had curious hats of beech-leaves on their heads. They glanced at us sharply and my companions saluted respectfully. Then the riders cantered ahead again the golden tunics softly fluttering. No one spoke at all. There was a great stillness in all the world, and yet a magic of close-interwoven life.

The road now began to be full of people, slowly passing up the hill towards the town. Most were bare-headed, wearing the sleeveless woollen shirt of grey and red, with a red girdle, but some were clean-shaven, and dressed in grey shirts, and some carried tools, some fodder. There were women too, in blue or lilac smocks, and some men in scarlet smocks. But among the rest, here and there were men like my guide, quite naked, and some young women, laughing together as they went, had their blue smocks folded to a pad on their heads, as they carried their bundles, and their slender, rosy-tanned bodies were quite naked, save for a little girdle of white and green and purple cord fringe that hung round their hips and swung as they walked. Only they had soft shoes on their feet.

They all glanced at me, and some spoke a word of salute to my companions, but no one asked questions. The naked girls went very stately, with bundles on their heads, yet they laughed more than the men. And they were comely as berries on a bush. That was what they reminded me of: rose-berries on a bush. That was the quality of the people: an inner stillness and ease, like plants that come to flower and fruit. The individual was like a whole fruit, body and mind and spirit, without split. It made me feel a curious, sad sort of envy, because I was not so whole, and at the same time, I was wildly elated, my rushing sort of energy seemed to come upon me again. I felt as if I were just coming to plunge into the deeps of life, for the first time: belated, and yet a pioneer of pioneers.

I saw ahead the great rampart walls of the town – then the road suddenly curved to a gateway, all the people flowing in, in two slow streams, through the narrow side entrances.

It was a big gateway of yellow stone, and inside was a clear space, paved mostly with whitish stones, and around it stood buildings in the yellow stone, golden-looking, with pavement arcades supported on yellow pillars. My guides turned into a chamber where men in green stood on guard, and several peasants were waiting. They made way, and I was taken before a man who reclined on a dark-yellow couch, himself wearing a yellow tunic. He was blond, with the trimmed beard and hair worn long, cut round like the hair of a Florentine page. Though he was not handsome, he had a curious quality of beauty, that came from within. But this time, it was the beauty of a flower rather than of a berry.

My guides saluted him and explained briefly and quietly, in words I could only catch a drift of. Then the man looked at me, quietly, gently, yet I should have been afraid, if I had been his enemy. He spoke to me, and I thought he asked if I wanted to stay in their town.

'Did you ask me if I want to stay here?' I replied. 'You see, I don't even know where I am.'

'You are in this town of Nethrupp,' he said, in slow English, like a foreigner. 'Will you stay some time with us?'

'Why, thank you, if I may,' I said, too helplessly bewildered to know what I was saying.

We were dismissed, with one of the guards in green. The people were all streaming down the side street, between the yellow-coloured houses, some going under the pillared porticoes, some in the open road. Somewhere ahead a wild music began to ring out, like three bagpipes squealing and droning. The people pressed forward, and we came to a great oval space on the ramparts, facing due west. The sun, a red ball, was near the horizon.

We turned into a wide entrance and went up a flight of stairs. The man in green opened a door and ushered me in.

'All is thine!' he said.

My naked guard followed me into the room, which opened onto the oval and the west. He took a linen shirt and a woollen tunic from a small cupboard, and smilingly offered them to me. I realized he wanted his own shirt back, and quickly gave it him, and his shoes. He put my hand quickly between his two hands, then slipped into his shirt and shoes, and was gone.

I dressed myself in the clothes he had laid out, a blue-and-white striped tunic, and white stockings, and blue cloth shoes, and went to the window. The red sun was almost touching the tips of the tree-covered hills away in the west. Sherwood Forest grown dense again. It was the landscape I knew best on earth, and still I knew it, from the shapes.

There was a curious stillness in the square. I stepped out of my window on to the terrace, and looked down. The crowd had gathered in order, a cluster of men on the left, in grey, grey-and-scarlet, and pure scarlet, and a cluster of women on the right, in tunics of all shades of blue and crocus lilac. In the vaulted porticoes were more people. And the red sun shone on all, till the square glowed again.

When the ball of fire touched the tree-tops, there was a queer squeal of bagpipes, and the square suddenly started into life. The men were stamping softly, like bulls, the women were softly swaying, and softly clapping their hands, with a strange noise, like leaves. And from under the vaulted porticoes, at opposite ends of the egg-shaped oval, came the soft booming and trilling of women and men singing against one another in the strangest pattern of sound.

It was all kept very soft, soft-breathing. Yet the dance swept into swifter and swifter rhythm, with the most extraordinary incalculable unison. I do not believe there was any outside control of the dance. The thing happened by instinct, like the wheeling and flashing of a shoal of fish or of a flock of birds dipping and spreading in the sky. Suddenly, in one amazing wing-movement, the arms of all the men would flash up into the air, naked and glowing, and with the soft rushing sound of pigeons alighting the men ebbed in a spiral, grey and sparkled with scarlet, bright arms slowly leaning, upon the women, who rustled all crocus-blue, rustled like an aspen, then in one movement scattered like sparks, in every direction, from under the enclosing, sinking arms of the men, and suddenly formed slender rays of lilac branching out from red and grey knot of the men.

All the time the sun was slowly sinking, shadow was falling, and the dance was moving slower, the women wheeling blue round the obliterated sun. They were dancing the sun down, and dancing as birds wheel and dance, and fishes in shoals, controlled by some strange unanimous instinct. It was at once terrifying and magnificent, I wanted to die, so as not to see it, and I wanted to rush down, to be one of them. To be a drop in that wave of life.

The sun had gone, the dance unfolded and faced inwards to the town, the men softly stamping, the women rustling and softly clapping, the voices of the singers drifting on like a twining wind. And slowly, in one slow wing-movement, the arms of the men rose up unanimous in a sort of salute, and as the arms of the men were sinking, the arms of the women softly rose. It gave the most marvellous impression of soft, slow flight of two many-pinioned wings, lifting and sinking like the slow drift of an owl. Then suddenly everything ceased. The people scattered silently.

And two men came into the oval, the one with glowing lamps hung on a pole he carried across his shoulder, while the other quickly hung up the lamps within the porticoes, to light the town. It was night.

Someone brought us a lighted lamp, and was gone. It was evening, and I was alone in a smallish room with a small bed, a lamp on the floor, and an unlighted fire of wood on the small hearth. It was very simple and natural. There was a small outfit of clothing in the cupboard, with a thick blue cloak. And there were a few plates and dishes. But in the room there were no chairs, but a long, folded piece of dark felt, on which one could recline. The light shone upwards from below, lighting the walls of creamy smoothness, like a chalk enamel. And I was alone, utterly alone, within a couple of hundred yards of the very spot where I was born.

I was afraid: afraid for myself. These people, it seemed to me, were not people, not human beings in my sense of the word. They had the stillness and the completeness of plants. And see how they could melt into one amazing instinctive thing, a human flock of motion.

Etruscan dancer, worked in wool by D.H. Lawrence and Frieda

I sat on the ground on the dark-blue felt, wrapped in the blue mantle, because I was cold and had no means of lighting the fire. Someone tapped at the door, and a man of the green guard entered. He had the same quiet, fruit-like glow of the men who had found me, a quality of beauty that came from inside, in some queer physical way. It was a quality I loved, yet it made me angry. It made me feel like a green apple, as if they had had all the real sun.

He took me out, and showed me lavatories and baths, with two lusty men standing under the douches. Then he took me down to a big circular room with a raised hearth in the centre, and a blazing wood fire whose flame and smoke rose to a beautiful funnel-shaped canopy or chimney of stone. The hearth spread out beyond the canopy, and here some men reclined on the folded felts, with little white cloths before them, eating an evening meal of stiff porridge and milk, with liquid butter, fresh lettuce, and apples. They had taken off their clothes, and lay with the firelight flickering on the healthy fruit-like bodies, the skin glistening faintly with oil. Around the circular wall ran a broad dais where other men reclined, either eating or resting. And from time to time a man came in with his food, or departed with his dishes.

My guide took me out, to peep in a steaming room where each man washed his plate and spoon and hung them in his own little rack. Then my guide gave me a cloth and tray and dishes, and we went to a simple kitchen, where the porridge stood in great bowls over a slow fire, the melted butter was in a deep silver pan, the milk and the lettuce and fruit stood near the door. Three cooks guarded the kitchen, but the men from outside came quietly and took what they needed or what they wanted, helping themselves, then returning to the great round room, or going away to their own little rooms. There was an instinctive cleanliness and decency everywhere, in every movement, in every act. It was as if the deepest instinct had been cultivated in the people, to be comely. The soft, quiet comeliness was like a dream, a dream of life at last come true.

I took a little porridge, though I had little desire to eat. I felt a curious surge of force in me: yet I was like a ghost, among these people. My guide asked me, would I eat in the round hall, or go up to my room? I understood, and chose the round hall. So I hung my cloak in the curving lobby, and entered the men's hall. There I lay on a felt against the wall, and watched the men, and listened.

They seemed to slip out of their clothing as soon as they were warm, as if clothes were a burden or a slight humiliation. And they lay and talked softly, intermittently, with low laughter, and some played games with draughtsmen and chessmen, but mostly they were still.

The room was lit by hanging lamps, and it had no furniture at all. I was alone, and I was ashamed to take off my white sleeveless shirt. I felt, somehow, these men had no right to be so unashamed and self-possessed.

The green guard came again, and asked me, would I go to see somebody whose name I did not make out. So I took my mantle, and we went into the softly-lighted street, under the porticoes. People were passing, some in cloaks, some only in tunics, and women were tripping along.

We climbed up towards the top of the town, and I felt I must be passing the very place where I was born, near where the Wesleyan Chapel stood. But now it was all softly-lighted, golden-coloured porticoes, with people passing in green or blue or grey-and-scarlet cloaks.

We came out on top into a circular space, it must have been where our Congregational Chapel stood, and in the centre of the circle rose a tower shaped tapering rather like a lighthouse, and rosy-coloured in the lamp-light. Away in the sky, at the club-shaped tip of the tower, glowed one big ball of light.

We crossed, and mounted the steps of another building, through the great hall where people were passing, on to a door at the end of a corridor, where a green guard was seated. The guard rose and entered to announce us, then I followed through an antechamber to an inner room with a central hearth and a fire of clear-burning wood.

A man came forward to meet me, wearing a thin, carmine-coloured tunic. He had brown hair and a stiff, reddish-brown beard, and an extraordinary glimmering kind of beauty. Instead of the Egyptian calm-ness and fruit-like impassivity of the ordinary people, or the steady, flower-like radiance of the chieftain in yellow, at the city gates, this man had a quavering glimmer like light coming through water. He took my cloak from me; and I felt at once he understood.

'It is perhaps cruel to awaken,' he said, in slow, conscious English, 'even at a good moment.'

'Tell me where I am!' I said.

'We call it Nethrupp – but was it not Newthorpe? – Tell me, when did you got to sleep?'

'This afternoon, it seems – in October, 1927.'

'October, nineteen-twenty-seven!' He repeated the words curiously, smiling.

'Did I really sleep? Am I really awake?'

'Are you not awake?' he said smiling. 'Will you recline upon the cushions? Or would you rather sit? See!' – He showed me a solid oak armchair, of the modern furniture-revival sort, standing alone in the room. But it was black with age, and shrunken-seeming. I shivered.

'How old is that chair?' I said.

'It is just about a thousand years! a case of special preservation,' he said.

I could not help it. I just sat on the rugs and burst into tears, weeping my soul away.

The man sat perfectly still for a long time. Then he came and put my hand between his two.

'Don't cry!' he said. 'Don't cry! Man was a perfect child so long. Now we try to be men, not fretful children. Don't cry! Is not this better?'

'When is it? What year is this?' I asked.

'What year? We call it the year of the acorn. But you mean its arithmetic? You would call it the year two thousand nine hundred and twenty-seven.'

'It cannot be,' I said.

'Yet still it is.'

'Then I am a thousand and forty-two years old!'

'And why not?'

'But how can I be?'

'How? You went to sleep, like a chrysalis: in one of the earth's little chrysalis wombs: and your clothes turned to dust, yet they left the buttons: and you woke up like a butterfly. But why not? Why are you afraid to be a butterfly that wakes up out of the dark for a little while, beautiful? Be beautiful, then, like a white butterfly. Take off your clothes and let the firelight fall on you. What is given, accept then –'

'How long shall I live now, do you think?' I asked him.

'Why will you always measure? Life is not a clock.'

It is true. I am like a butterfly, and I shall only live a little while. That is why I don't want to eat.

The Ship of Death

Lawrence worked on 'The Ship of Death' in his last months, splitting off sections to stand as separate poems in the volume published posthumously as Last Poems. *These poems and their variant drafts are one of his greatest achievements, but the attitude of acceptance and calm which pervades them is not new. As early as 1916 Lawrence concluded an essay on 'Life' with the words:*

> Do I fear the strange approach of the creative unknown to my door? I fear it only with pain and with unspeakable joy. And do I fear the invisible dark hand of death plucking me into the darkness, gathering me blossom by blossom from the stem of my life into the unknown of my afterwards? I fear it only in reverence and with strange satisfaction. For this is my final satisfaction, to be gathered blossom by blossom, all my life long, into the finality of the unknown which is my end.

Frieda Lawrence was with him at his death:

> I held his ankle from time to time, it felt so full of life, all my days I shall hold his ankle in my hand.

The Ship of Death

1
Now it is autumn and the falling fruit
and the long journey towards oblivion.

The apples falling like great drops of dew
to bruise themselves an exit from themselves.

And it is time to go, to bid farewell
to one's own self, and find an exit
from the fallen self.

2

Have you built your ship of death, O have you?
O build your ship of death, for you will need it.

The grim frost is at hand, when the apples will fall
thick, almost thundrous, on the hardened earth.

And death is on the air like a smell of ashes!
Ah! can't you smell it?

And in the bruised body, the frightened soul
finds itself shrinking, wincing from the cold
that blows upon it through the orifices.

3

And can a man his own quietus make
with a bare bodkin?

With daggers, bodkins, bullets, man can make
a bruise or break of exit for his life;
but is that a quietus, O tell me, is it quietus?

Surely not so! for how could murder, even self-murder
ever a quietus make?

4

O let us talk of quiet that we know,
that we can know, the deep and lovely quiet
of a strong heart at peace!

How can we this, our own quietus, make?

5

Build then the ship of death, for you must take
the longest journey, to oblivion.

And die the death, the long and painful death
that lies between the old self and the new.

Launch the Small Ship, by Blair Hughes-Stanton

Already our bodies are fallen, bruised, badly bruised,
already our souls are oozing through the exit
of the cruel bruise.

Already the dark and endless ocean of the end
is washing in through the breaches of our wounds,
already the flood is upon us.

Oh build your ship of death, your little ark
and furnish it with food, with little cakes, and wine
for the dark flight down oblivion.

6
Piecemeal the body dies, and the timid soul
has her footing washed away, as the dark flood rises.

We are dying, we are dying, we are all of us dying
and nothing will stay the death-flood rising within us
and soon it will rise on the world, on the outside world.

We are dying, we are dying, piecemeal our bodies are dying
and our strength leaves us,
and our soul cowers naked in the dark rain over the flood,
cowering in the last branches of the tree of our life.

7
We are dying, we are dying, so all we can do
is now to be willing to die, and to build the ship
of death to carry the soul on the longest journey.

A little ship, with oars and food
and little dishes and all accoutrements
fitting and ready for the departing soul.

Now launch the small ship, now as the body dies
and life departs, launch out, the fragile soul
in the fragile ship of courage, the ark of faith
with its store of food and little cooking pans
and change of clothes,
upon the flood's black waste
upon the waters of the end
upon the sea of death, where still we sail
darkly, for we cannot steer, and have no port.

There is no port, there is nowhere to go
only the deepening blackness darkening still
blacker upon the soundless, ungurgling flood
darkness at one with darkness, up and down
and sideways utterly dark, so there is no direction any more.
And the little ship is there; yet she is gone.
She is not seen, for there is nothing to see her by.
She is gone! gone! and yet
somewhere she is there.
Nowhere!

Beyond, by Blair Hughes-Stanton

8
And everything is gone, the body is gone
completely under, gone, entirely gone.
The upper darkness is heavy as the lower,
between them the little ship
is gone
she is gone.

It is the end, it is oblivion.

9
And yet out of eternity, a thread
separates itself on the blackness,
a horizontal thread
that fumes a little with pallor upon the dark.

Is it illusion? or does the pallor fume
A little higher?
Ah wait, wait, for there's the dawn,
the cruel dawn of coming back to life
out of oblivion.

Wait, wait, the little ship
drifting, beneath the deathly ashy grey
of a flood-dawn.

Wait, wait! even so, a flush of yellow
and strangely, O chilled wan soul, a flush of rose.

A flush of rose, and the whole thing starts again.

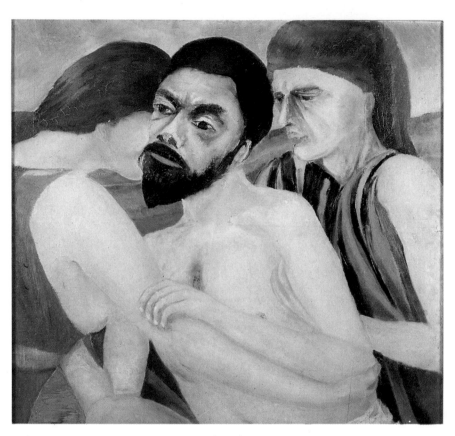

Resurrection, by D.H. Lawrence

10
The flood subsides, and the body, like a worn sea-shell
emerges strange and lovely.
And the little ship wings home, faltering and lapsing
on the pink flood,
and the frail soul steps out, into her house again
filling the heart with peace.

Swings the heart renewed with peace
even of oblivion.

Oh build your ship of death, oh build it!
for you will need it.
For the voyage of oblivion awaits you.